Praise for *Memorial, 29 June*

'This is clever writing. Høeg clutches achingly at the bonds of youth gone by and pulls the strings of her story with ease. Hoekstra conveys in a buoyant translation.'
– Martin Aitken, literary translator

'With an uncanny ear for line breaks and an eye for emotional vulnerability, Tine Høeg draws a tender portrait of the friendship between Mai and Asta, confirming that the past tentacles into the present, whether we want it to or not.'
– Anna Stern, author of *all this here, now*

'*Memorial, 29 June* is a breathless read, delivered in pin-sharp prose. An understated novel of repressed love, grief and longing – and a subtle essay on the creative process. Høeg deftly reveals Asta's hidden and written stories in tandem, from the first glimmer and restlessness of beginning, through urgency and self-isolation and denial, to the defining moment of declaration. Gorgeous.'
– Sonia Overall, author of *Eden*

'Intimate and diamond-sharp, both in style and wit. Høeg takes us to the raw, tender, and absurd intersection in a writer's life of what is, what once was, and what still could be.'
– Saskia Vogel, literary translator and author of *Permission*

'Høeg writes with arresting wit and subtlety. Sharp yet delicately drawn, *Memorial, 29 June* is a tender study of living together and apart, and a compelling meditation on creativity, grief and yearning written with startling precision.'
– Sussie Anie, author of *To Fill a Yellow House*

Memorial, 29 June

Memorial, 29 June

Tine Høeg

Translated from the Danish
by Misha Hoekstra

Lolli Editions
London

for my best friend

I get an invitation to a memorial gathering, 29 June at Blossom to-day or today?

sorry, I know you're writing

I'll stop pestering

you coming over tomorrow?

Bertram misses you

was it tonight you had a date?

Your boyfriend's a cad for being so late

two old men playing pool
the one comes over and stands before me

well I say

he isn't my boyfriend

I'm sitting on a high bench against the wall
I've bought two beers and almost finished mine

then he's a cad *and* a fool. Cheers

cheers I say

he keeps standing there

you look goddam gorgeous

he smiles

a small tuft of hair poking up oddly from the centre of his
scalp

one doesn't leave such a lovely lady waiting

I smile back

it annoys me not to be able to touch the floor

Jørn, the other man shouts

it's your turn!

they try to impress me with their play
measuring angles, aggressively chalking their cues

Wrecking Ball on the stereo

and a table of young teens in the corner
boarding school kids maybe, playing dice and
singing along. Tinsel's draped above the bar

it's the end of April
I've just turned thirty-three

the third stage of youth

I read that somewhere

I finish the bottle and weigh
drinking the other beer too

then he arrives

in a way-too-warm jacket, his hand feels dry

we met on Tinder
he's a documentary filmmaker

prefer shadows to sun, Burroughs
to Bake Off and I've read more books
than most, he wrote in his profile

awful

but then there was a photo
where he squinted a bit with one eye

young man

Jørn's there right away pointing his beer at him

and I'm chuckling

because the documentary filmmaker's
forty-three and divorced with two kids

you're simply ill-bred

the documentary filmmaker looks confused

you don't let a dish like this sit and grow cold

my laughter rings out loud and strange
and I feel suddenly irresistible

toothsome and savoury

and I hop down from the bench
have an urge to turn everything up
the music, my feelings, to kiss him
and buy a long line of shots, make something light up

but then

hours of plodding dialogue

I ask and ask

and when I say something his gaze drifts
and focuses on something somewhere behind me
so I'm tempted to turn and check out
what it might be

he crosses one leg over the other and looks at me

so what about you and kids?

I take a pull on the beer he's bought

it's wheat beer

I don't like wheat beer
it tastes foul and yeasty

what do you mean?

well is it something you've thought about?

I take another pull

you want to have kids?

yeah

the boarding school kids shriek with laughter, one of them
has said something funny, the pool players have gone home
the bartender flashes the lights off and on

or no

last call!

I push back my chair

maybe

fine he says and grabs a handful of peanuts
because I just need to be straight with you

I've had all the kids I'm going to

he throws them into his mouth

so it's just not in the cards

he chews and chews

for me

to have a kid with you

I'm a writer

I'm working on my second book

a novel about the Polish portraitist Lysander Milo

I'm sitting at the computer with earplugs in
the flat next door is being totally renovated

Milo worked in a cement factory

in Bydgoszcz in the sixties

one day he vanished, age twenty-three
and in a big basement room they found more than
a hundred busts in cement, sculpted in secret
depicting a cross-section of the factory workers

a few years later Milo turned up in Warsaw

he had a huge breakthrough
before he disappeared again for good

Bydgoszcz

how do you even say that?

I massage my temples

the workmen have been at it for three weeks
tramping up and down the stairs
starting early in the morning with their steel-toed boots

Sweet Dreams Are Made of This

and the radio blasting, today they're drilling into something

I page through photos of the busts

they're eerily beautiful

I saw them by chance last winter in Berlin and
was captivated. The faces rough and simplified

yet at the same time inscrutable

soulful

I could stare at them forever

live people in cement

they study me as much as I study them

I take a deep breath

the drilling grows louder

the coffee in my mug moves almost imperceptibly

I visit Mai almost every day

but tell me more about your date she says

we're watching Peppa Pig on the sofa, Bertram between us

she lives alone with him

the flat smells of fabric softener

it's one huge shambles

what went wrong, was he ugly?

no

so what then?

it's just that I detest dating I say
it leaves me cold, anyway
I left you some Bolognese in the freezer

you're a peach Mai says, did you kiss?

no

you shag him?

God no

oh how boring and she fumbles for her phone
what time is it, will you eat with us?

I've actually got to go I say

I need to go home and write while it's quiet

about that concrete sculptor?

it's cement I say

when are you going to be done?

I don't know. A long time yet

it's an obnoxious question, Mai

we'll have to throw a big party!

she moves Bertram's arms as if he's dancing
he doesn't take his eyes from the screen

and tonight we'll have pizza

she kisses his hair

because Mummy's lazy, can you say pizza?

I don't talk to him enough
you're supposed to talk to them all the time

simply constantly

so they get a big vocabulary

and do singing games so they develop a rhythmic sense

he's not even two I say
he'll talk when he's ready to

and we read to him all the time

you do she says

Bertram places a chubby hand on my thigh

Asta's got to go home now says Mai

can you say Asta?

Asta?

I run into Hannibal from my old floor
at the end of Holmbladsgade

hilarious he says

it's been a dog's age
you live out here now?

his acne's gone, else he looks the same

and congrats goddammit

he punches me on the shoulder. With your book!
I saw you in all the papers, I'd no idea
you wrote, did you do that back then too?

ehh I say and point

what've you got in the bag?

it's actually a nappy pail

he scratches beneath his cap

I'm going to be a fricking dad

here in September, it's totally bizarre

putting up fibreglass mesh

steel beams and fireproof insulation

he talks on and on excitedly, his girlfriend's
a midwife so it was destiny sort of, they've just
torn down a wall, it's a real science

and how goes it with you on that front?

not much to report I say

but I'm totally okay with that

it's not something I go around searching for

of course not he says

I guess you've got lots of other irons in the fire
hey by the way, are you going to Blossom?

I can't alas

downer. What about Mai?

I think she's doing something else too I say

well

yeah

he raises the bag and smiles

I should probably be getting home with this thing

Pierre 41, schoolteacher
perched on a unicycle

Karl-Kristian 39, butcher
standing with an arm around his mum

Søren 37, hedonist and consultant

I've been swiping all evening
I ought to write on my novel

but I swipe and swipe

Sebastian 42, self-employed
doing a side plank at the water's edge

Lasse 36, mischievous sports masseur

Marco 44, optician. No anal

ingen anal, keine Anal, pas d'anal
geen anale, sem anal, brez anal

I hurl the phone away, I feel loathing

for all humanity

I pick up the phone again and delete Tinder

I have an urge to cry
or rake someone over the coals

but I don't know whom

you asleep?

not yet

you see the invite?

why didn't you say something?

what invite?

from Sif, on facebook

didn't see anything

what's she inviting to?

a memorial get-together
for August at Blossom
because it's ten years now

all of us from the floor

you still awake?

At first I kept thinking I saw him

Mai adjusts the folding top

at the supermarket for instance or
cycling across Knippelsbro, can you
check if there's any sun on his face?

he's fine I say

it could've been something about their hair

or their shoulders she says

their way of moving

we've gone for a walk in Bispebjerg Cemetery

to show Bertram the cherry trees
in bloom. He's sleeping like a stone

can you remember that time in Ikea

Mai takes a puff on her e-cigarette

when it suddenly smelled of his cologne?

yes I say

it was like a bit resiny she says

we're quiet for a while

I think you ought to be careful I say then

about opening that door again

what did it say on it again?

on what?

on the kitchen door she says

those newspaper headlines

I don't remember

yes you do she says. You remember everything

is that a mother and daughter I see walking there?

a shabby man on a bench smiles at us

no Mai laughs

yes the man says, he's got red hands
he sits and fiddles with a plastic bag

we're friends I say

no he says suddenly sharp

the mother's got the eyes
and the daughter the hair
and the grandchild in the pram

you're mother and daughter he says

and once more, louder

you're mother and daughter

he stands up, now he's furious

mother and daughter!

we pick up the pace, I glance over my shoulder
he's swinging the bag in a circle over his head

we break into a run

mother and daughter he shouts

and the grandchild in the pram!

Golonka, babki

I'm in a good mood

I'm googling Polish food

and have ordered ear defenders
designed for roughnecks on oil rigs

kapusta, piernik

a wonderland of splendid names!

sernik's a cheesecake, kluski a kind of dumpling

I glance at the time

I'm supposed to guest a TV book show
this afternoon. I really want to finish
a lunch scene at the cement factory

four hours later I'm standing before the mirror

angry and desperate

I'm in a mad rush

I have greasy hair and I'm wearing slippers, I got lost
in recipes and culinary traditions, I've written one line:

there's no kluski in the clear soup

I'm not going to make it to the studio
it's totally unrealistic

I've got to call and say I'm sick

there's no kluski in the clear soup

sure, I could read that to the audience

a cracked tooth, it has to be something acute

a stomach ache

something no one wants to catch

And I can see you've already had a go at it

the makeup artist takes hold of my chin

I try to smile, my back's wet with sweat
I cycled here at full tilt blasting Believe
by Cher to pump myself up

she inspects my face critically

then lets out a deep sigh

well all right, she turns
and rummages in a drawer full of brushes

we'll just have to spackle it over

and I suppose you're scribbling away at something new?

the makeup artist rolls across the floor
I'm draped in some kind of cape

I really loved your first one

she tugs the stopper from some liquid eyeliner

but such a pity for her
at the end, is this a sequel?

not really, I clear my throat

I'm writing my way into a Polish sculptor

okay she says, now hold your head still

from the sixties

okay she says again, look down

isn't that a bit of a slog?

not at all I say

the process is actually quite rewarding
I've got a ton of material

on Poland. And the time period

and cement

she wrinkles her brow

I mean he started by working in cement

ahh she says. Look up

and then it's tremendously liberating
to write about someone else I say

to be transported completely out of your own head

I'm beautiful when she's done
I don't look like myself

my gynaecologist for instance, her nail polish is always flaking

I tell the host a short time later

we're seated in two designer chairs talking about
how as an author you gather
and store details for later use

the audience laughs, the cameras whirr

now I don't want to leave the stage

but actually it was Mai's gynaecologist

it's something *she* told me

I can't stand Bertram's smell

in the afternoon
when we come home

that institutional smell

reminds me of back when
I was a teaching assistant in Tårnby

                                        The Time Machine

imagine if I'd become a teacher

                            wasn't the preschool called that?

                            where you were working

yep

                            who comes up with those names?

I've fled to a café for some peace and quiet

next to me sits a guy
watching a movie about flying cars

it's extremely distracting

I scroll through my manuscript

I only have seven pages of real text

on the other hand I've got twenty-four
about social conditions in Poland
a folder on cement plus essays
and analyses of Milo's portraits

I study a bust of an older man

with deep-set eyes
and a look I can't fathom
shifting back and forth
from mournful to mischievous

how could anyone form such a face from cement?

the elegance in those coarse features

I google my old halls of residence
a sudden impulse

the building hasn't changed

my chest hurts

the guy with the cars is eating cappuccino foam

with a teaspoon excruciatingly slowly

But how's it going with yours?

I'm having drinks with Monica

we know each other from a writing workshop
she just had her first chapbook accepted
and traded Jensen for her middle name

the collection's called Methuselah, Methuselah

I'd rather hear more about yours
I say and sip my mojito

when's it coming out?

well offhand we're thinking October

she smiles and touches up her lipstick

but it depends a bit on how long it takes
to settle on the cover, I'm talking with a photographer
who's really obsessed with heather. Hey

she waves a hand before my face

anybody home?

sorry I say

I think I know that guy over there

where?

behind you. Don't look

she turns with her glass

the tall one?

yes

who is he?

someone I knew once

someone who lived on my floor at uni

they're sure sitting close Monica says

that's because he talks very quietly I say

his name's Niels Klit

she raises an eyebrow

you can't be called that

a short time later he leaves the bar with a curly-haired woman

he doesn't see me

it's started, Asta

my mum's on the line, her voice thin

my aunt's been ill a long time

she's taken a sudden turn

I pace in circles with the phone
open all the windows in the flat
till at last I lie down in the middle of the floor

she's losing altitude

that's what the doctors told my uncle yesterday

I stare up at the ceiling. Then the air raid siren goes off

I find myself screaming

oh honey my mum says

it's just a drill

each of us quiet on our respective ends

it goes on and on
the tones shifting

sounds stir-crazy, dithyrambic

I shut my eyes

I want it to stop

can they hear it at the hospital?

yes my mum says

I should think so

In the afternoon my mum calls again

my aunt is dead

it happened right in the middle of the siren she says

I tried calling

you at your publisher's?

just wanted to say I'm sorry about your aunt
God and check out something strange

I'm on the bus going home
from the job centre and then I see Gregers

through the window

I rap on it and wave each time
we pull up to a light but he doesn't see me

business suit and bike helmet
he must be raking it in

remember how he always ate those sandwiches?

The publisher's on the fourth floor

come in and tell me about this art novel of yours

my editor's invited me to lunch
I just want to know roughly where you are
he wrote in the email. I don't want to go

I step into the lift

a woody cologne hangs in the air

with a whiff of alcohol

I have to lean against the wall

I can see myself in the mirrors

from every side simultaneously

the light stutters

it's been that way forever says Mai

we climb steadily up and up

to the fifth floor. Ta-da!

she pushes open the door with her shoulder

she's lived on the floor two months
and gone steady with August one and a half
the first time they kissed was
Easter dinner in the kitchen

curried herring and dill schnapps

she sounded so happy the next day that
I had to stand up with my phone

right this way she says

a glass door, a long corridor

Mai's the one who got me the room

it smells of fishcakes and damp floors

Linda 5A she says and points

nutrition and health, always whingeing
about the racket from the lift

Sif 5B, political science

she's super cool

and the storeroom on the end
the door jams sometimes

Gregers 5C, something in the business school

hi Hannibal!

a burly guy with acne and a water bottle
pops out of a room

you going down to work out?

yep

this is Asta says Mai

who's moving into 5F

definitely he says

baseball cap and a warm hand

he disappears through the glass door

down there's where I live, she points

and then it's you

and beyond that August

and Kim on the end
he's our ghost. Come!

she pulls me by the arm

the kitchen's here

the empire of desire it says on the door

don your destiny like a jacket

and in all caps

MORE AMOUR LESS MERDE

the kitchen's cramped

a bench, a table
an oven and four burners
some Christmas lights and a disco ball

a guy with a buttoned shirt and spiky hair wipes his fingers
on a napkin

Gregers he says and stands up

in front of him on a plate are three identical sandwiches

corned beef and aspic

Asta I say

sorry I'm just up to my armpits in this critter

a sturdy girl by the counter
is grinning. So you get an elbow

Sif, hi

Asta

she seems to be a dab hand with the chicken

lovely to meet you she says

want to join us? There's baked potatoes too

actually I'm just here to see the room

she doesn't move in till tomorrow says Mai

and wasn't it something about Danish lit?

Sif slides a pat of butter up under the skin

yes starting in September I say

you could've said she was coming today
a guy in an apron flicks water at Mai

I'd have made myself presentable

August, pleased to meet you

his hand's wet

his face alert

still just Asta

la vista he says

Mai laughs, the tap runs

the feral and the domestic

it says on the cupboard over the sink

rise and shine

we are the answer to the crisis

You can just cover that with a rug

Mai stands in the middle of the room

and it'll feel lots larger soon as
you get some furniture. She crosses
the floor. And just check out the view

she opens the door to a French balcony

birches galore!

I think they're aspens I say

what's that up there?

a sleeping bag she says

it was hanging there when Gregers moved in
we tried knocking it down with a football

well so anyway

she turns to me

expectation in every movement

how do you like him?

I just feel like it's been inflating

Linda has long hair and heavy eyelids

as if people think their clothes pegs give them
carte blanche to let their dishes stand out for days
and I just feel that that wasn't at all the idea
when we started the peg system

my first floor meeting

we sit squeezed around the table

electric kettle and instant coffee

agreed says Sif

she's moderator and secretary both

she has a prestigious internship in
the Ministry of Social Affairs, prepping conference rooms
today she brought home ballpoint pens
and a freezer bag full of leftover chocolates

it's not called inflation says Hannibal

he's studying social science at Roskilde

Linda glares at him

stop acting like King Quibble, how long
has that pot for instance been by the sink?

it's soaking he says and sticks his hand in the bag

we also discuss a newspaper subscription

my life in the Red Guard says Gregers

he's the only one who votes for the financial paper

I want to assert myself in the discourse

but don't know how

the others' faces are connected
with yarn and thumbtacks
to a big heart on the bulletin board

5th middle it says there in gold marker

as the one in charge of the salt I guess it's
Hannibal who has the last word

we talk fine and kosher

yes please

he points to his mouth as he chews
what do you actually call these things?

cat tongues

it's the first thing I've said

my face flushes

what kind of contribution is that

cat tongues

but Hannibal just nods and grabs another handful

yum he says and the conversation continues

Mai guffaws and tightens her ponytail

she has on a pink blouse with a boat neck
she keeps looking over at August

he's sitting with his hands behind his head

I will him to lean forward
and touch Mai's bare shoulder blade

and then he does

moths and larvae

the possibility of reserving one cutting board for onions

Hannibal fetches beer

you can't taste the difference anyway
after the first one he says to a proposal to replace

Harboes with Tuborgs

everyone says cheers

did anyone actually call Kim?

yeah but he doesn't answer

we're going to table that says Sif
to the topic of tinfoil

well friends, she clicks her pen

last point on the agenda

bingo Thursday, who's in?

I listen outside the door the next morning

stand there and collect myself before I open it

but the kitchen's deserted

I feel relief and disappointment

crumbs on the table and an open newspaper
a wooden butter knife with a clothes peg on the lip of the sink

we'll dance till we die

every cupboard is decorated with clippings
every floormate has their own. I swipe
a piece of crispbread from Mai

it tastes good, it's got cinnamon

if God were a powerful woman
it says on Sif's cupboard and on Linda's:

the parsnip principle

Gregers has lived here longest, his is completely covered

coins are like the blood in your body

I can't make any sense out of that line

Dr. Strangelove. August is studying medicine

my door is unadorned

I wonder if the previous resident took his clippings
when he moved out, in a plastic sleeve say

I wonder what it'll end up saying on mine

you were here!

Sif's suddenly in the doorway, a bag over her shoulder

did you see?

she points to the bulletin board, I just
used your profile pic from Facebook

you're officially a member of the family now

In Netto everything bulges

the bell peppers are large and crisp

the temperature in here's comfortable

there's only me and a little old lady
each of us wheeling our trolleys around

the cinnamon crispbread's on sale
how lucky can you be

I grab three packages

pick out a white wine, feeling grown-up

Liebfraumilch

I stumble across a red ceramic bowl in a bargain bin
it's nice and cheap. They have everything
a heart could desire

hand soap, pretzel sticks

at the checkout there's trouble with the receipt printer

just a sec says the teenage checker

no rush I tell him. You need help?

nah it's just the roll

I smile at the old lady and feel
connected to everything I see

a part of some immense system

she stands beside a tall stack of shopping baskets

her hair thin and white

it rises very slowly as we wait

static electricity

she doesn't notice

the entire left side

in the end it stands up vertically

I feel a jolt of joy as if
everything in me's cracked open

then the machine clicks

it emits a rotary and
highly satisfactory sound

We're three to a fridge

Hannibal's shelf is a mess

processed cheese and bacon and a plastic tub
of pasta salad that looks past its date

Gregers has mostly packages of cold cuts

pork loin and rolled meat sausage, smoked ham

arrayed in a row

I put my items in place, it looks good
I open and close the door a few times

I pour a bag of apples into a plastic mixing bowl

free for the taking!

that's my first entry in the kitchen journal

love Asta

then I rub out Asta and write 5F

the way I see the others do

I invite Mai to a little housewarming

oh she tells me on the intercom
I said I'd go for a walk tonight with August
in a little while, you playing Anne Linnet?

three knocks when we've hung up

her voice, then his

I turn down the music and listen

two distinct registers

footsteps and laughter

the glass door

then it goes quiet

I open the door to the balcony. Not a breath of wind

I fetch the white wine and pretzel sticks and
a stemmed glass. I arrange it all on the floor
seat myself on a cushion and glance about the room

I feel a heavenly calm

the bookcase

the wicker chair and the desk

the room key

which I've placed in the red bowl
that'll be the key's assigned spot

on the windowsill's a cactus

a home. My hand

that raises the glass,

my items in the fridge

and Mai out there in the golden light

the wine's chilled

and the pretzel sticks!

I'm almost weeping

what a wonderful and simple invention

The days are long and quiet

the others attend classes and work part-time

I read the paper and do crosswords
wash the dishes and go shopping a lot

I begin to bake rolls

experiment with seeds, different kinds of flour

it feels peaceful

the swelling dough

I sit before the oven and watch

place the rolls in a basket
beneath a tea towel, walk around excited
for the others to come home

I smelled them all the way out in the lift says Sif

wicked delish says Hannibal
you pass me the butter please?

I sit beaming at the end of the table

Mai invites me out to the Carlsberg Visitor Centre

she wants to see the draught horses

August is coming too, it's free
she says, we meet in the lobby at four

you going in?

he holds the door open for a pale woman

no thanks

such a gentleman, Mai ruffles his hair

and always attentive he says

she laughs and zips up her jacket

I really don't know if I'm cut out
Mai says when we're out on the avenue

to teach little kids

she's a teaching assistant at a preschool in Tårnby

today for instance she says and lights a cigarette

I dropped this huge padlock out in
the shed with the roller skates. Do you know
how soft some of those kids' skulls are?

did it hit anyone?

August leaps up on a rock

no says Mai and puts the lighter
in the pack. But I got totally stressed

I study a girl with no head or left arm

August crouches before a mermaid

it turns out the visitor centre has a sculpture garden

this face is well made he says

check out the look in her eyes

I mean how long can you stare at that hunk of iron?

Mai's already reached the end of the garden

it's bronze August says

yeah yeah she says, but shouldn't we find the horses?

it's warm and quiet in the stalls
like stepping into another time

the light pours down from the skylights overhead

the horses all look identical

enormous sorrels with white manes

Akselvinge and Toffer

their names on small brass plaques

Herkules, Lambada, Blue Moon

Mai guffaws

this one's called Asta

no it isn't I say

yes it is. See for yourself

we crowd round the horse
it stands there peacefully chewing something
then it snorts and both of them laugh

aw little Asta, Mai strokes its muzzle

such a sweet horse

she glances at me. Hey are you upset?

no I say. It's just idiotic

that's not a horse's name at all

Theoretically

Gregers sips his coffee, he's no right
to just go around knocking on doors

we're gathered in the kitchen

someone down on first saw the TV licence inspector
the internal phone chain has been activated

Hannibal came charging up from the workout room
to hide his flatscreen behind the freezer, now he stands
in his sweaty T-shirt frying up frozen hash browns

I don't get how you can stand that basement

Linda's in tights and running shoes
she's training for a half marathon
with her sister on third

it's so gross and stuffy she says

we just got new dumbbells

Hannibal tips the hash browns out of the frying pan

and the carpet's been cleaned

you see him?

August has been out on the stairs to see what's happening

nope he says. Strange says Mai

I actually feel bad about not paying
Sif says and hangs up a dishtowel

Linda regards her

I just don't feel that it's fair for pensioners to get a break
she goes to open the window, ponytail swinging
when we don't she says and shouts down to her sister

I'm coming!

then she turns to Hannibal, who's shaking out ketchup

let me just tell you something

you won't get anything out of lifting
if you sit there stuffing your face

she points at his plate

with junk like that
you should eat protein

and a lot more veggies

it'd also be good for your skin

they ought to just add it to your tax bill says Sif

that night Gregers hears from two girls on fourth

that it wasn't the licence inspector at all
but someone's dad in a conductor's uniform

who came by to drop some keys off

Grand prize is a month's rent

we're seated at long tables in the lobby
draught beer in plastic cups and crepe paper from the lights

the mood is giddy

give me more of those

no the orange ones!

Hannibal's bought ten cards, he's feeling stressed

there are red splotches on Sif's cheeks

Mai rocks back and forth and chants

number twenty number twenty
come on number twenty!

a guy in angel wings turns the large cage
two girls with glitter on their cheeks cry out the numbers

Gregers has won a free repair of a bike puncture
Linda a portrait of some Chinese bride and groom
and August a stuffed fox

nighmber nunteen! shout the glitter girls in chorus

thirty-five. Forty-three!

mix them up!

fourteen they cry. Eighty. Seventeen!

bingo yells a girl in glasses from first

a fanfare starts to play, a surge of boos
everyone from seventh throws their tokens

then there's a break

the toilet queue is long

August stands right in front of me
he's got the fox under his arm

I'm feeling light-headed and a bit tipsy

I want to say something to him
to express the connection
we have through Mai

but I can't come up with anything

I've never spoken to him alone

he doesn't speak either

Jette in any case is going to have a Jägermeister

a guy with a large Adam's apple places
an order with a girl who's heading to the bar

she makes a beeline for it

and a brewski for me and René!

brewski I say to August

that's the ugliest word I know

he looks at me

brewskis and cat tongues

then he hands me the stuffed fox

can you just hold him while I piss?

we're born with all our teeth

I'm heading out the door, Mai

they hide up in your gums

in two rows

just try and google it

I'm going to a performance

with Monica?

yeah

you can see it on X-rays

to-day I was thinking about

if you had a baby
and moved in with me

today

The artistic duo's called Kelp and Emerald

you've got to promise to keep an open mind says Monica

we trot up the stairs, we're running late

no socks or shoes

the performance is taking place in
a private flat, a bulky man
with a nose piercing welcomes us in the hallway

he hands us each a glass of wine

why can't we keep our socks on?

he regards me gravely

it's a rule unfortunately

just come on says Monica

the audience sits barefoot on the floor
around Kelp and Emerald, who are situated
on two stools in the middle of the living room

they both have their eyes closed

the one is making rhythmic plashing sounds with a bottle
the other has a small lump of dough on his shoulder

I take a sip of wine

it's sour

sparkling slime is being kneaded on a big screen over the sofa

it's hot in here. And there's a weird smell

maybe owing to all the feet

I picture Mai's face if she were here

Monica elbows me in the side. Shh!

the man with the lump of dough pulls on
slowly and sensuously, a pair of yellow rubber gloves
and starts to eat an apple into a microphone

the audience watches him raptly

the champing's intense

I fold my arms, remain standing there awhile

then I turn towards Monica

I'm going to go outside and wait

three pints I shout

timing and time

we've gone to a bar and fallen into conversation with
a building engineer, his hair is receding
and he lives in Hedehusene, I can't work out
whether he's got a family or not

and a splash of malt syrup

he's obsessed with baking his own black rye bread
he tells us about it with great zeal

hey!

he slaps a palm on the bar
you can get a splotch of sourdough from me

I don't eat bread says Monica

it's more than fifty years old he says

thanks for the offer I say

and then I tell the building engineer about
Kelp and Emerald, he has to wipe his eyes

Monica looks a bit annoyed

it was a sensory exploration she says

when I get up to visit the toilet
the building engineer lets his hand
brush across the small of my back

you've got a men's bike he says

we walk together down Alhambravej, he's looking for his car

it's three in the morning

there's no way you can drive to Hedehusene now I say

you're plastered

he stumbles over the curb, I have a sudden desire for sex

oh for Christ's sake he says panting
I'm sitting in the backseat with my blouse up over my breasts
he's fighting with a baby seat

in a moment of clarity I see the scene from outside

where you going?

he peers out at me befuddled

thanks for tonight I say and swing my leg over my bike

take a taxi home

I've thought about August a lot

Mai sets the nail polish down by the coffee table

I'm giving Bertram some milk, he holds the bottle himself

since we got that invitation she says

okay I say and caress the hollow
in the nape of his neck

he was very like, hmm

she blows on her fingers

sexual

if you can put it that way

his whole being

a sort of wild energy that made it so I
just all the time wanted to gobble him up

is it wrong to say that when he's dead?

of course not I say

Bertram's neck muscles move
rhythmically as he drinks

something presses against my pelvic floor

don't you remember at parties Mai asks

how jealous I could be?

Cloudburst on my way home

I seek cover in front of a block of flats

excuse me

a man leaps onto the top of the steps

red beard and light blue shirt
shoulders dark with water

it looks beautiful

as though the fabric's shimmering

I'll just scooch my buttock over

thanks, he fumbles in his pocket

but I live here actually

ahh okay. We both laugh and
he inserts a key in the door

I'll just scooch my buttock over

it echoes in my head when he's gone

buttock buttock buttock buttock

then suddenly he comes back out and makes me start
he smiles at me and opens an umbrella

I watch him walk down the sidewalk

he brought down a canvas tote from Irma

strange weather to go shopping in

maybe he expects guests tonight. Sure smells good
his sister says in the hallway, where should I put the wine?

I stand there for twenty minutes
waiting for him to return

consider taking a picture of the intercom

then I walk out into the rain

I'm freezing when I get home

when I position myself at a certain angle
under the showerhead, it looks as though

water's spurting from my nipples

The entire evening I just lie there and stare into space

I'm in an odd humour

I get a text and perk up a bit
but it's from my mum:

how'd you like to inherit our extra toilet
next January? We can probably have Ib
install it, he'll be retired by then

Mai goes to a café with me to send off job applications

she bangs on the keys
she's been unemployed since her maternity leave ended

I'm in the middle of a scene with a cement mixer

God damn I'm cranking them out

she takes a sip of coffee
how's it going there with you?

ouch for fuck's sake

she sets down her mug again
doesn't seem like you're writing very much

I look at her. Sorry, she raises her eyebrows
and wipes some drops off the table with her napkin

at first I thought it was blood

a gaggle of girlfriends are eating tapas behind us

they're talking very loudly

but it was just the mucus plug going, can you pass me the
tapenade?

aïoli and crackers, cradle cap and olives

I can't concentrate

the one's had some of the umbilical cord frozen

stem cells she says and peels the strip of fat
from a slice of Serrano ham. If for instance he
goes and gets leukaemia

what time are you reading tomorrow Mai asks

seven thirty

then twenty thousand kroner is nothing

perfect says Mai, my mum'll look after Bertram

I mean seen from *that* perspective

now I'm freaking out

over what she said about the stem cells

should I have done that too?

Are you on first?

Mai looks around the bookstore

I'm number four, so after the break

super she says, do I have time to go out and vape?

the first reader is young and stands too far
from the mic. He has trouble finding his place
in his sheaf of papers, and his hair hangs in front of his forehead

I feel a great tenderness towards him

the second writes novels with very difficult titles
and looks incredibly irritated when he reads. As if
it's a huge annoyance that the audience is here

Mai sits a long time with her brow furrowed

then she leans over

does this take place on a spaceship?

don't think so I say

the third reader pauses interminably
after the title of each poem. He's brought an electronic
musician who plays the sound of raindrops

and galloping horses

Mai fidgets in her chair

I make an effort not to look at her

good grief she says outside during the break
I wasn't into that at all, she takes a sip
of her coke and turns to two young women

it was like being at a funeral, don't you think?

an intriguing collaboration

I hear myself say to the poet with the hoofbeats
I don't really know why I say that

he just nods and sucks deeply on his cigarette

the irritated one sets a beer bottle down on the stairs

it'll be good now to have you on stage he says

so the evening doesn't get too existential

we go to The Clown's Bodega after the reading

the irritated one sits at the head of a table and holds forth
Mai's gone home to relieve her mother, I stand at the bar
with the young reader and the guy who owns the bookshop

he's friendly and rather short

we talk about electric boogie, both of them went to it
as kids. We laugh a lot and take turns buying rounds

you'll really have to show me your moves

later that night I'm walking down
Nørrebrogade with the bookseller

hold my bike he says

then he throws himself onto the pavement

and does a pathetic version of the worm
he completely fails to get his lower body to follow
I laugh out loud and some saliva goes down the wrong pipe
he gets to his feet and pounds me on the back

at the next intersection he asks

weren't you supposed to live in Amager?

well I say, it's not that far to walk

we keep talking, he's really not that short

I slip a piece of gum in my mouth

anyway

he stops his bike

I turn off here

I mean we could also
I slap his bike seat

have another beer? Someplace or other?

oh he says, that sounds lovely
but I'm afraid I can't

or maybe just split one?

it's just not going to work, he turns on his rear light

I try to catch his eye
my hand still resting on his saddle

he looks up and smiles

I've got to go home and hit the sack he says

my girlfriend has a birthday tomorrow

have fun last night?

it was ok

anybody cute?

nah

well

what kind of a bloody question is that to ask I mean
excuse me but as if it'd be a stroke of luck if only I
could meet some random arsehole as if that's why
I talk to people what a ridiculous life dream no that
isn't what it's all about falling in love and reproducing
it just makes me want to puke I mean everyone gets
divorced anyhow or cheats and everyone's going to
die anyhow and then you're supposed to RAISE
someone and then you feed them oatmeal and bananas
and then they can stand up how MARVELLOUS and
then you go around and feel like there's some MEANING
BEHIND IT ALL but there's no bloody meaning just
try for once to see it from a bigger perspective
I mean oatmeal and bananas oatmeal and bananas
it makes no difference use your effing brain it's just
springtime and springtime and springtime into
fucking INFINITY and the world's gone completely
to the dogs and you don't even use your compost
bucket I mean WAS ANYBODY CUTE??????

I receive a parcel in the post with a jam jar of sourdough starter what was it called

the thing August died of?

the heart disease

hello just answer

something with a b?

Brugada's

oh right

I didn't ever say
a proper thankyou

for what?

for getting me dressed

and feeding me

for sleeping in my bed

every night for so many weeks

for all that you did back then

Mai, stop it

I want to go
to Blossom, Asta

I know

We hold a funeral for my aunt

my cousin has her eyes
she blinks and blinks

a muscle working in her cheek

my uncle's grown thin

my other cousin fiddles with the hymnal

he lives in Berlin and has a girlfriend who
does pottery, she rests a hand on his thigh
they're heading back Tuesday

it's soothing to think about

ceramics. A plane takes off

the minister's hair is coppery, she speaks quietly

as if she's afraid of waking someone who's asleep

can you even fit, Asta?

I'm driving with my mum's cousin after
the service and her new husband Karlo
who's quite corpulent. My mum's cousin
works at a plant nursery in Brøndby Strand

I'm sitting in the backseat
along with five big bags of soil
one of them on my lap

can't you scoot your seat up a bit, Karlo?

really I'm fine I say from behind the bag

and are you getting any writing done my mum's cousin asks

we worry about you sometimes
it's a precarious path you've chosen
that's also what I told your mother in the narthex

and then being all alone

Asta's an author she says to Karlo

oh ho, he turns in his seat

have you written anything I'd have heard of?

the wake is a couple of miles from the chapel

schnapps and open-face sandwiches

red eyes around the circular tables

thank you my cousin says

she's breastfeeding in a corner, I hand her
a Napoleon hat on a paper plate

how are you doing?

she sets down the pastry

I really don't know she says
I haven't really had time to think about it
she puts a nursing pad in place

because of her here

she buttons her blouse with her free hand
anyway, would you mind holding her?
I've got to pee

my cousin's daughter's called Molly

she's heavy and warm

I stroke her nose with my thumb

her skin's so soft that
I almost can't feel it

Karlo's stood up on the far side of the room

he is headed for the table

he has a way of leaning back when he moves
as if his paunch were a bass drum

I'll give you a tip

he plumps down beside me

one of my old employees published a book
about home brew, may I?
he's pointing at the Napoleon hat
and I'll be damned if there doesn't turn out
to be money in that rubbish

he downs half of the pastry in one bite

so you could you know think about that

he takes another bite, leans back and spreads his legs wide

I've had lots of people under me in my time
he chews and swallows. Before the slipped disc

you maybe heard about that

no I say. Rocking and rocking

well he says, picking up the crumbs
with his finger, but you have now

I've thought about writing a book myself

he sighs deeply

but it's simply just that business of
finding the time. Yeah they're sweet those ones
he nods at Molly and pours himself a schnapps

how old is it you are again?

thirty-three I say

he raises his glass

I imagine that the clear fluid is poison

tick-tock he says

I let myself in around midnight

my flat smells of rye bread

I stand awhile in the hallway with my coat on

then I go out to the kitchen and knock
the loaf from the form, it's still warm
I swaddle it in a tea towel

and take it in my arms

it has a wonderful weight

I can't fall asleep

the cement factory seen from the outside at dusk
a large selection of busts, a map of Bydgoszcz
and a photo of Lysander Milo he took with a timer

I get up and print out a stack of pictures

pin them on the bulletin board in the living room

and in the middle in all caps: his name

that'll be the book's title

very simple, I knew that much from the start

I take a step back and look at Milo

there aren't really any self-portraits in his oeuvre
which is unusual. Only this one photograph

so distinct from his other works

contrived, posed

his gaze is serious, almost arrogant
directed straight into the camera
yet it's as if he's not looking at me

what is he looking at?

I stand there a long time studying him

then I open a new document:

I get an invitation to a memorial gathering, 29 June at Blossom

what's going on?

I've called 5000 times

why don't you answer?

HELLO ASTA!

now I'm getting worried

It's not because I'm mad at you says Mai

I think it's brill it's going so well
with the concrete book, it's just that I miss you
do you carry this with a glitter top?

we're at Fisketorvet

we haven't seen each other in four days

I've been writing from morning to night and already
I long to get back to my manuscript
it's budding, thriving, expanding

at a terrific rate

I haven't told Mai that I'm writing something else now

we could stop by Dalle Valle and have some cake?

we're on the escalator with our bags

I think I'll head home I say with a sinking feeling in my gut

yeah, I don't really need any either says Mai
but let's just pop our heads into Monki, it'll just take a sec

she assembles an immense pile of clothes

I sit down on a pouf outside the changing room

she draws the curtain

my legs are restless

I can't get comfortable
there's a tic under my eye

a long time passes

how's it look on me?

she steps out in a turquoise sequined dress

it's short and tight

we're looking for costumes for the disco party
in a small second-hand shop on Istedgade

it smells here of powder and mildew

yes I say, it's amazing

tulle and barrettes

beads, ties and stilettos

we spend a long time drifting among the racks

Mai also tries on a fur

hey did I tell you that August's mum is an artist
she asks and sniffs the one sleeve

no I say

what kind of artist?

installations I think says Mai

hey what about these here?

she pulls a pair of platform shoes
from a shelf. They've got your name on them!

they're not me at all I say

they *are* you

I refuse to smell like a bodega! Don't you get that?

Linda and Hannibal are arguing when we get back
she slams the kitchen door and shouts from the corridor

you're a sick egocentric!

a recurring debate

whenever Hannibal smokes in his room
the smoke seeps through the thin wall of his hallway
and into Linda's closet

she's lost her marbles he says
and slices open a bag from the freezer

it's not my responsibility

he pours the contents into a skillet

it makes an awful stench

he stirs it with a wooden spoon

you see it's some sort of structural issue
he says and looks deeply unhappy

I suppose you think it's my fault?

Mai wrinkles her nose. What are you frying?

chicken liver from the store, his face brightens for a moment

it's pure protein

What reeks in here?

Sif's home late from the Ministry of Social Affairs

Hannibal's liver I say

Mai and August are revising skin layers

stratum basale he says, stratum spinosum

correct says Mai. They sit across from each other while
I drink coffee and do a crossword

go on she says

stratum, hmm. Wait. Granulosum?

we've got to remember by the way to buy lasagne sheets
says Mai. For Friday, we promised Sif

stratum granulosum or what?

that's right she says. Next

stratum lucidum and stratum corneum

perfect, and she claps the book shut

how do you actually remember all that
I ask. I mean the medical terms

Britney Spears glows like candy says August

I furrow my brow

it's a mnemonic he laughs

for dermatology. You use the first letters

mm I say, that's clever

what the heck says Mai

you've done a lot

August tugs the crossword towards him

may I?

oh no, Mai rolls her eyes
I mean, shouldn't we hit Netto?

but I think I made a mistake up here

I point

end of the line in eight letters

that's singular of course

so it doesn't seem like it should end in S

no I can see that
he scratches his eyebrow with the pencil

that's a problem

Mai gets to her feet. Jesus, you guys are so boring

but *budding season* in six he says
can't really be anything but SPRING, can it?

exactly!

I lean across the table

I don't get it

In the middle of the night I get a text from August

CURTAINS!

Oh my *God* this itches

Mai tugs down on the sequined dress with one hand
she's standing by the window and smoking
there's a strong smell of Red Door in the room

you *are* using an old lady deodorant I say

she laughs and blows a plume of smoke

that's because I'm really a shrivel inside

her lips are pink and her hair crimped

is that really even disco I ask

what?

crimped hair, isn't that more eighties?

it doesn't matter says Mai

oh wow, Linda looks her up and down
when we step into the kitchen. You've gone all out

she's wearing a black cocktail dress

the lasagne's too salty

we eat baguettes and drink vodka sunrises

the guys have all bought gold suits online
in some thin tight-fitting material
Sif's put on purple eyeshadow and made a playlist

the mood escalates steadily

for Christ's sake, Kim, come and sit down!

at nine o'clock the door opens

everyone whoops and claps

I've only met Kim a few times before
he studies philosophy, is partial to beige
and eats most meals in his room

howdy all

he's wearing an Afro wig

I didn't think you'd come Sif says and hands him a beer

yeah he says, I didn't think I would either

at midnight we go down to the party in the lobby

a chaotic mass of decked-out students

cheap bar and strobe lights

oops sorry

August has touched my shoulder with his beer bottle

it's cold, it gives me shivers

hey, aren't you at the med school?

a girl in a white pantsuit leans
towards him and starts chatting him up

I go over to the others

I just don't think it's fair
Linda sucks on her straw, I'm probably the person
who uses less onions than anyone

they're discussing who buys what groceries

we'll have to take it up at the next meeting says Sif
and rubs her eye, oh no, did I smear it?

Mai isn't listening

she's watching August and the pantsuit girl
they're speaking intently into each other's ear

cheers I say

Mai doesn't respond, her eyes narrow

hold this

she hands me her drink

she veers across the floor

she says something to the girl, who looks deeply offended

then she drags August away

onto the dance floor

I sink into a sofa and watch them

they close-dance, a sparkly four-legged creature

anyone sitting here?

some dude plops down beside me

you are I say

he's got very long thighs

what are you drinking?

I've actually no clue, I take a sip
of Mai's drink. Sloe gin fizz I say
and raise the plastic glass

cheers

cheers he says. Niels Klit

what?

my name's Niels Klit

I look at him

you can't be called that

he majors in maths, lives on tenth middle
and talks incredibly soft. His mouth hardly moves
he grew up ten miles southeast of Aalborg

somewhere called Lillevorde

what?

Lillevorde he says

like little wart?

he looks confused

I don't think so
my parents still live there

we sit for a while

want to dance?

I don't dance I say

he takes a swallow of beer

me neither

I play football

I write poems

then I get abruptly to my feet and leave the party

I've never told anyone that before

the lift's blocked off, I take the stairs
two steps at a time, let myself into my room
kick off my shoes and lie down on the bed

it goes quickly

gold and sequins, the orgasm hurts

a long stab up through my body

when I get back the sofa's empty

I can't find Niels Klit

August sits cross-legged on a picnic table
out on the lawn, the pantsuit girl is waving her cigarette
she laughs and reaches for his beer
he watches her as she drinks

people smoke and shout, a guy pukes in a hedge

inside the party's peaking

Mai's dancing with Kim, they're up on a windowsill

two girls lean on the bar and watch them

that's her from up on fifth says the one
she thinks she's in a music video

she's totally tanked says the other

and what's with the eighties hair?

shut your traps I say and take a swing at their drinks
lime slices and umbrellas fly into the air
they shriek and leap back

I get frightened too

stand and stare at my hand

then I turn on my heel

what the hell do you think you're doing
I hear them shout after me

crazy cow!

the kitchen's deserted

the bass thumps through the floor

I pace back and forth
open and close my fists
breathe rapidly

I'm upset and don't quite know why

then the door's kicked open

it's Kim

he enters dragging Mai with him
she's got blood all over her face

she fell he says panting

out on the stairs

I rush over and lift her chin
she lurches around on her platform shoes

oh no says Kim, it's gushing almost

it's just a nosebleed I say
and feel instantly at ease

get some frozen raspberries

he looks at me

or strawberries I say. That she can suck on
it'll make the blood vessels contract

this was really the only thing there was

Kim's back with a bag of peas

we place Mai between us on the bench

I pinch her nose just below the bony bridge
Kim feeds her cautiously with a teaspoon

she grunts a good deal

she smiles at me crookedly through her hair

what the hell, did you kill her?

the others come bursting in a short while later
there's blood all the way up the stairs says Hannibal
it's like *The Shining*

rinse it out right away

I tell August when we've got Mai
into her room, he lowers the blinds
Kim's cleared off the bed and fetched a bucket

the sequined dress lies on the floor

in cold water I say
else she'll never get the blood out

okay says August without turning around. Thanks

I think of the girl in the white pantsuit
the way she waved her cigarette around
and I get an urge to strike the back of his knees

see him buckle

or no I say, give it to me

I rub and wring at the kitchen sink
my hands grow red with cold

Kim stacks dirty plates and empties bottles

we move the table back in place, vacuum
and do the dishes, shake out the purple velour tablecloth

the others have gone to bed

we don't say much

he turns on the radio and fiddles a long time with the fre-
quency
then finds some classical music and seems satisfied

Schubert

I don't realise until a little later
that that's what he said

it's grown light out when we finish

I open the door to the French balcony

the party's over, the first birds

I lean forward a little

two people are kissing by the bike racks
the guy's got a mountain bike between his legs
she must have stopped him on his way home

I feel all of a sudden ancient

somewhere behind me Kim makes a sound

then he places his hands on my hips
and turns me around, he's removed his wig

for a moment we stand like that

with our lips pressed against each other
swaying gently to violins

then he releases me

he smells of soup

Please, Asta

Mai talks me into going with her to see a football match

August is playing for the halls team
an intramural tournament in Fælledparken

nutmeg shouts a guy with a knee brace

the match is already underway when we walk across the field

which ones are we asks Mai

she's wearing hoop earrings and a high bun

I've just spotted August

the red I say

now he sees us too

Mai waves avidly, he picks up his pace

a clump of spectators sits on a blanket

they're from Grønjord Halls and have beer and soft drinks

what's the scores asks Mai

score says a girl in face paint
and espadrilles. It's called what's the *score*

I find myself laughing, the girl shoots me an angry look

well then what's the *score* says Mai

two nil us says the girl with satisfaction and takes a nip of her
Fanta

we sit on our jackets further down the sideline

come on boys! Mai claps her hands
and pulls a bag of crisps from her backpack

Niels Klit is playing for us as well

he's easy to spot, he's the tallest on the field

and very quick

that surprises me

heads up for number seven!

elegant, almost floating

a tall brushstroke

number seven!

as if he sees lines and patterns in the game
invisible to the others

a hard low shot hits the goalpost

stay on seven dammit

the Grønjord goalie spreads his arms

a few minutes later Niels Klit scores

the ball nestles all the way up in the corner

the others leap on him, shouting and whooping
and mussing up his hair. He looks happy

almost embarrassed

we're cheering too. August casts us a sidelong glance

then he shifts into high gear, sprinting back
and forth, fighting for possession
rolling around on the grass, getting up and gesturing

he's not very good at football

it looks exhausting

let's see some cynicism, boys
says a guy with a ponytail at halftime

the players stand in a circle a distance

calves and thighs

sweat and dirty shorts

August wipes his face with his jersey
I can see his abs

then Niels Klit waves at me

where do you know him from?

just someone I talked to at the party

he's handsome says Mai

his name is Niels Klit, and you can't be called that

Mai laughs and yawns out loud. Sorry
she shakes her hair. I'm a bit tired

we talked all night, you want the last ones?

no thanks I say

I'm only sitting here because I'm in love
she says and jams the crisp bag into her backpack

football's the boringest thing in the world

what did you talk about?

you name it she says and scratches at a stain on her jeans

and then he read me something

you mean from a book?

hmm, she spits on her fingertips
no, something he wrote

I turn to face her

how do you mean wrote?

Out on the lawn that evening we set the table

are those cheese dogs?

Linda leans over the grill

there's also normal ones says Hannibal

we drink rosé and discuss stuff like ketchup brands

I'm having a hard time taking part in the talk
the whole time I keep looking at August

it's as if I've never seen him before

this one's really raw

Sif's sliced into a chicken breast

the charcoal hasn't really caught
Hannibal fetches lighter fluid
we eat the pasta salad while we wait

but it's only a rumour

Gregers has heard that the caretaker has a glass eye

we've got to remember by the way to clean the grate says Mai
because of rats, otherwise he'll have a fit

my grandfather had twelve toes says Kim and everyone laughs

no but check this out says Sif

I once made out with someone who was missing an arm

and I didn't find out till the second date

So what was it about?

we stand in the lift with the dirty plates

what was what about?

what August read you I say

the thing he wrote

I don't know says Mai

well you must have some idea

I can't remember, Asta
she laughs and shoulders open the door
or I can't explain it

maybe something about a water tower

a water tower?

Around midnight I google

water tower

though I don't know what good that'll do

I get up and walk around my room
sit back down again, I spin around a couple of times
on my desk chair, I open a new file
and close it, I go look in the mirror by the door

then I log onto Facebook

                                                    hey August

a message pops up as I press send

hey Asta, nice of you to come
to the game, regards Niels K

It's hard to be around Mai

it feels as though I'm deceiving her

defrauding her

do you have a bladder infection?

I keep having to go out to the bathroom to make notes

everything can be utilised and connected

I hope not I say and slip my phone
into my pocket, should we just do those dishes?

if I can dry she says

still going good with the concrete book?

Mai opens the utensil drawer

maybe you'll read me some soon
it feels kind of lonely sometimes she says
not being a part of what you're writing

it's as if you disappear somewhere else

I'm right here you know. I scrub a plate energetically
by the way, did you get an answer from Michael about the
birthday?

she looks gloomy. Of course not

Mai's ex is a brand manager for Asics and has his father's face
tattooed on his chest. So is his dad dead I asked
when she told me, nah he lives in Ishøj
but it's fricking weird when we have sex

Mai got pregnant after four months
and Michael didn't want the kid

change of subject

she bangs the drawer shut

I'm starting a paid traineeship

cool I say and empty the dishpan of dirty water

where?

City of Copenhagen says Mai

some department called Properties & Procurement
she puts a pot away in the cupboard
it was Ulla who got it for me

who's Ulla?

my advisor at the job centre

the one with the chin?

she nods

when?

already Monday

I've totally forgotten how to do it all

pack a lunch, chat with people

it kind of stresses me out, Asta

they probably have a cafeteria, hey

that one's not quite clean

it doesn't matter she says

I'll get the last bit with the dishtowel

I beg off everything

Monica gets angry
my mum gets angry
a librarian in Vanløse gets angry

I don't care, I'm writing

if I venture out I keep
having to stop and take notes

or I simply turn around and go home

like my mouth is watering

but in my brain. That's how it feels

I find a note from when Bertram was born

the smell on the maternity ward: blood and Marie biscuits

I force myself to go to Næstved

a talk at the high school

I already feel peevish on the regional train
the toilet's occupied the whole trip and I'm
almost sure I saw two people go in together

youthhostel

I glower out the window

recyclecentre

I sit there getting steamed up over the misspellings passing by

WORK SHOP

why don't they make a little effort
before they go and order some giant sign?

the shoddiness of the world

I'm simply going to have to stop you again

in the auditorium there's problems with the PA

a Danish teacher in a tweed jacket has leapt
onto the stage, nobody's heard my intro

an AV tech is summoned, restlessness in every row

I stand there for an eternity, exposed with my papers

ladies and gentlemen

the Danish teacher taps on the mic
and extracts another round of applause from the students

showtime he says and winks at me

just take it from the top

the talk goes terribly

I'm not present at all

I tell my jokes wrong
and don't connect my points

pause and stammer and leave dead air

the teachers blow into their coffee cups

the students doze

hundreds of peacock eyespots stare at me
from a skirt in the first row

a fury suddenly surges up in my body

what the hell is this
to have to stand here like some lousy comic

to pander to teens, pearls before swine!

when all I want is to write

a tidal wave sweeps across the rows

and carries off every living creature

when I picture that from up on stage it goes easier

well I say when it's finally ten o'clock

any questions?

utter silence

don't be shy now

the Danish teacher in the tweed jacket has glided up
beside me without my noticing

we look out across the hall

come on people, he claps his hands once

a boy in the back shifts in his seat

yes, the Danish teacher nods encouragingly

the boy rubs his eye

how much money do you make?

two girls want to take a selfie with me

I try to smile naturally

afterwards they stand there tapping on their phones

the one looks up

what was your name again?

how'd it go today?

at the department

and what is it
you do concretely?

this innovation centre's opening in Nordhavn
and I'm supposed to help organise it
I'm in charge of the service agreements for

pads fruit milk and coffee

mouse pads?

scouring pads

today I had to send
an email with the heading

re: inspection of pads

Asta?

I run into Linda in Rema 1000

I've been writing for eight hours straight
I'm in PJs with no makeup
wandering the aisles like a zombie

she's in the produce section feeling avocados

long time

she looks me up and down

then her sister appears with a bottle of mineral water

they're totally unripe says Linda and then to me

so how's the glamorous writer's life?

both of them gawk at my basket while I speak

it's full of instant foods and Pepsi Max

hey, you going to that memorial get-together?
Linda turns to her sister, you remember
the guy who had a stroke

it wasn't a stroke I say

he had a congenital heart condition

yeah yeah Linda says

called Brugada's syndrome I say

well but anyhow stone-cold dead on the kitchen bench she says
and cops and doctors everywhere on the floor, ugh
I'm so glad it wasn't me who found him

she flips her hair

in a way it was good it was Sif, was it you
that tried to do CPR?

no I say and have an urge to punch her in the mouth

it was Kim

she rolls her eyes. Kim!

I totally forgot about him

she turns to her sister again, you remember
the psychology guy who always wore beige

my jaw tenses

he studied philosophy I say

just imagine if *he* shows up says Linda

kind of obnoxious it's at Blossom, it's so smoky
didn't you two actually have something going?

me and Kim?

you and August

I stare at her

no

definitely not

oh, she shrugs her shoulders

I just thought you did

you asleep?

no

it was so strange

that night. At the tour de chambre

think if I hadn't been
stuck in that storeroom

if I could have done something

Mai

we've talked about this a million times

no one could have done anything

I know that

I just wish
he hadn't been alone

SITTING ALL ALONE

oops sorry

in a room with 300 potted plants

waiting for some man to come
and quality inspect them

everything's called quality inspect

the burial

I almost can't
recall anything

mostly his mum's face

and that it was way too sunny

thanks for getting him

Naw, you've got a son!

I meet another author from my publisher
outside the nursery school

I had no idea

she bends over the pram

what's your name, little brisket?

aww she says and looks up at me
he's definitely got your nose

his name's Bertram I say

he'll be two in August

I hoist him onto my hip in the hallway
and stand before the mirror

That evening I sing him to sleep. Then I sketch his face

I'm inheriting my aunt's office chair

it was my mother's idea. It's *quality*

she told me on the phone

my aunt was a reflexologist

her furniture's stored in a remote warehouse

in front of the entrance at 2?
my uncle texted me
and sent a smiling sun

I arrive a little too early

I lean against a yellow wall and wait

I think about my novel
it's with me all the time

it sits and glitters in my chest

Asta!

my uncle waves and squints skyward

an iron gate shoots to the side, a breeze lifts his hair

we're going this way he says

a glass door, a long corridor

he's grown even thinner, almost transparent

his shirt's rumpled, and then it's straight on
and to the left, he walks with brisk strides
and attempts to strike a cheery tone

the furniture isn't stacked

it's positioned as if they were trying to furnish the space

it's *quality* as I told your mother
he rolls the chair to the middle of the floor
and claps the backrest. Take a load off!

it's eggshell colour and comfortably springy

I've never sat so pretty

it makes me happy that it'll get a new life
he says and smiles at me

his voice booms a bit

I feel as though we've found ourselves in a dismal
and surreal version of my aunt's clinic

thanks a million I say and smile back at him

I'm sitting like a dream

can I offer you anything, Asta?

my uncle glances around

or no. I can't, actually

don't worry about it I say

it was so lovely

he sits on the padded table and looks at me

didn't you think?

the funeral

beautiful I say, were those lilies of the valley?

we talk a long time about the minister and the weather
the hymns

her stuff says my uncle at some point
all her stuff. There's so unbelievably much of it

what do I do with it all?

then he slaps himself on the thighs

well he says and remains seated

how are you doing, really I ask

he looks suddenly forlorn

I don't actually know

then his face grows gentle once more

I'd rather hear how *you're* doing he says

when I saw you standing outside I thought you were so radiant

are you in love?

everything's abbreviated here

JKK TMF

SUF SOF

I don't understand a thing
I just sit there and nod

BUF BIF

just ate lunch with someone
called Susse from the coffee team

she's wicked sweet

her son's a butcher at Fakta

ohn dohn dehn
mama futter fehn
futter fehn mama dehn
ohn dohn dehn

remember that rhyme? what's it mean?

is it German?

My uncle drives me home

he helps me bear the chair up to my flat

and a dresser
a collection of matryoshka dolls
a table lamp, a recorder
a chess game, a woven basket
a framed poster of the sole of a foot
and a pale brown leather jacket
with a threadbare lining

he seems buoyed up when we say goodbye

trying to reckon

how much milk 2400 people
use in their coffee each week total

a pint apiece?
is that too little?

300 gallons of milk

what surprised me most
back then with August was how

death was so concrete

not mysterious

but totally physical

Mai shows up unannounced

suddenly she's there on the intercom

oh I say, actually now's not a good time

yes it is she says

just a quick cuppa, I got off early

I glance feverishly around the flat

then I bang my computer shut
slam my notes in a drawer and just manage
to rip a photo of our halls from the bulletin board

what the hell's with the foot?

she peels off her sweatshirt in the hallway

it was my aunt's I say

and what are those over there?

she heads straight for the matryoshkas
they're in a box in the middle of the floor

they're also my aunt's I say
she had family in Moscow

maybe they'd be something for Bertram?

Mai scoops up a doll

I really don't think so she says

they're hand-painted I say

completely authentic

she opens and opens and opens

shit this one's tiny

she examines the inmost one

then she puts it down and gets up

hey have you been out shopping?

she's caught sight of the leather jacket
draped over the back of a chair

well I say, that's actually not mine either

it's totally moth-eaten says Mai and sniffs at a sleeve

no but why'd you get all this junk?

I just did I say and go out to the kitchen
with a dirty plate

I need to escape her gaze

that's kind of stupid she says from the living room

and that over there isn't yours either
she must have spotted the dresser behind the door
you don't have room for it, Asta

it looks really cluttered

and why's it so gross in here?

now she's standing in the doorway, you're usually a neatnik

blood rises to my cheeks

her presence feels like an attack

an exposure

I haven't asked for her company

her opinions, her prattle

I want to be alone

alone with my manuscript
that's the only thing that matters

because I'm writing I say
and fling a fork into the sink

get it?

when Bertram was falling asleep he said your name

Heat wave in early June

the sun floods the living room

I can't see my screen

the workers are sanding, I only hear it now

I decide to take a break and bike to Helgoland

bellies and moles, thighs. I lie down
among the naked bodies in the women's area
knees and C-section scars. The smell of salt and sunscreen

I close my eyes

my skin grows warm and trembly
a vast receptive membrane

the lap of waves beneath the boards

fragments of text float up and vanish

I bob on the surface of sleep

excuse me for disturbing

someone taps me on the shoulder

but I'm just going to throw caution to the wind
a woman in pink Crocs crouches before me

Lone

she proffers a hand

I've been lying there spying on you a bit
she says and pushes her sunglasses up in her hair, actually
I just want to say I love your book

she has a purling laugh

so hurry up please and write another!

she speaks in a rush, a torrent of words

I struggle to tuck some towel
over me in an offhand way

chiefly rice and pasta production

she's worked in the foodstuff industry all her life
she didn't start reading books until she retired

and now I'm perfectly insatiable

she's just started a reading group for a bunch of women
whom she was stuck in a lift with
at Roskilde Library

an awkward ninety minutes she says

we both laugh. Then I catch sight of someone

off to the side behind her

kimono and pitch-black bob

my pulse quickens. It's August's mother

Lone keeps talking

I stare and stare

hey she says, are you okay?

then the woman stands up. Turns her head

I hold my breath

but it's not her at all

she must look completely different anyway
it strikes me now. Ten years older

last time I saw her was at the cemetery

I suddenly get tears in my eyes

I think I'm going to go for a dip now I tell Lone

thanks for chatting

of course she says and gets to her feet

I've just been squatting here anyhow
and running my mouth

the steps are green and slick with algae

I plunge

all sounds vanish

I want to remain down here

let myself be enveloped, dissolve

my chest starts to ache

then I push off from the bottom

Asta!

Mai calls from shore

we're going to the kiosk, you want anything?

finals are in full swing
the whole floor has cycled down to the beach
a study break or I'll keel over dead
said Sif this morning, now she shakes out her towel
Hannibal and Gregers toss a frisbee

August waves to me with a red wallet

we agreed to read each other our poems on Thursday

my fingertips tingle with the thought

yes please I shout

a ham and cheese toastie!

hey August

tomorrow
your place or mine?

you decide

yours then

check

how many poems are you
bringing and are we sending
them to each other beforehand?

texts

let's do them prima vista

Asta

check

I google prima vista

Ital. at first sight

musical discipline in which the player or
the singer is not familiar with the score in advance
and thus performs the music by sight-reading

I reread our exchange

he didn't answer how many

I print out the five I have
and read them aloud

sitting, lying down

the best one's about a stairway, it's very short

I stand in front of the mirror

changing tempo and emphasis

I knock on August's door at ten a.m.

I've got my poems in a plastic sleeve

I'm nervous

Asta he says and bows
his hair's rumpled and he's wearing sweatpants

his room's cave-like

dark and chaotic

you didn't need to clean up for my sake

he laughs and rubs his face

I move about with an inspectorial air

a flayed man in anterior and posterior view

four sketches of a boy
with a rabbit in his arms

the walls are plastered with art and anatomy

his eyes follow me

I regret the plastic sleeve

femur, tibia

arteries

the chambers of the heart

where'd you get that from?

over his bed's a large wall hanging
stunningly beautiful. It depicts two
anthropomorphic forms sprouting or growing

the tapestry? My mum made it

I thought she did installations

she does all sorts of things

did she do these too?

I point at the boy with the rabbit

yes he says

is that you I ask

is that important?

I don't know I say and step a bit
closer. It sort of looks like you

he shrugs his shoulders

so let it be me

he's mounted a box on the balcony
it's full of cigarette butts

a green thumb I say and again he laughs

what's in there?

upon the desk is a silver suitcase

twenty-four vertebrae he says
and lays it on the floor at my feet

I raise an eyebrow

you don't believe me?
well then open it

the lid opens with a click

the case is lined with dark-blue foam
each bone nestles in its own depression

they look like jewels or hand-carved figures

I pick up the smallest one
roll it between my fingers

my grandfather August says

I stare at him

relax he laughs, it's just a model

next to the case is a sparkly scrunchie
that I recognise. It's Mai's

THE DAYS

and a sheaf of papers that must be his poems

we become aware of it at the same time

my cheeks grow warm, August scratches his neck

should we just make some coffee first?

I'm actually supposed to be at a lecture he says
and pushes down on the French press. A long sinew
bulges in his forearm

the spinal column and back muscles he says and snorts

but this'll be a lot more fun

back in the room I blow on my coffee

well he says, Asta Canasta

I suppose we can't beat around the bush any longer

we settle ourselves across from each other on the bed

August clears his throat. Do you want to start?

uh sure. I smooth out my papers

I guess I could

cool, he runs a hand through his hair

we meet each other's eyes

then start to laugh

I haven't really done this before I say

what do I even do?

You look like someone who's been fornicating

I run into Hannibal as I'm
going back to my room

ha-ha I say. Very funny

I close the door behind me and look in the mirror

there are red splotches on my chest and throat

my eyes are shiny as if from fever

we talked about texts for four hours

I feel simultaneously
drained and completely over the moon

I stand in the middle of my room and start to laugh

louder and louder, almost hysterically

then I notice my telephone
it's blinking on the desktop

there are seven missed calls from Mai

and a voice message

I fling my bike down in front of the preschool

a police car idles by the entrance

and what time was that?

a tall officer is speaking with a male teacher
in ballet flats, well it must have been just before lunch

when does Elliot come back?

the teacher picks the boy up in his arms
soon he says and to the officer: so getting towards eleven
thirty

it smells of stew and lilacs

I can't see Mai

her message was incoherent

but I got the gist:

she forgot to shut the main door

a child disappeared

I think he's bored

a girl with dough-coloured hair crawls around on a bike rack

he's all by himself

a female teacher with red eyes
plops onto the ground beside her

and he didn't bring any toys

are you Elliot's mother?

an officer who's slightly less tall approaches with outstretched
hand

not me, I shake my head emphatically

then I spy Mai

she's leaning up against a shed at some distance
from the others, she's as pale as a corpse

she stares at me

he's dead she says when I get over to her

Mai, I grasp her by the shoulders

then her body starts to tremble

she squats down and stands up
brushes her hand across her mouth
spits and shakes her head

she won't meet my eyes

he's dead, I'm going to throw up

I try to hold her fast

she rocks back and forth

get me out of here she says

Mai I say. Look at me

we were going to paint them

paint who?

the stones she says

I was supposed to go out and collect stones, I don't
want to be here when they come

when who comes?

now she looks utterly insane

the parents she whispers

I cup her head in my hands

get me out of here, Asta. Before they come

a car swings across the gravel
we turn our heads simultaneously

it feels as if time almost stops

as if it's immeasurably heavy

solid and strange
outside itself

the driver's door opens in slow motion

a woman steps out

her eyes have a look I've never seen before

she stands there in the sun

she's wearing two different shoes

then Mai suddenly tears herself free
she walks straight up to the woman

it's my fault she says

her voice is clear and focused
and so laden with gloom that I can't breathe

I'm the one who didn't close the door

it's all my fault

with that a door bangs open
and a teacher comes bursting
from the preschool, waving a phone

Just try to explain it again says Gregers

we're eating spaghetti Bolognese

well Mai says and tears off a hunk of baguette

he left the preschool in Tårnby
and then he basically hiked all the way
to his mother's hair salon, she laughs loudly

suddenly he's just standing there in the doorway

would you please pass the Parmesan asks Sif

where's the hair salon?

on Amagerbrogade I say

that's quite a trek says Hannibal
how old's the boy?

four and a half says Mai and seems moved

just think that he could remember the way

like some homing pigeon!

hi Asta, I'd just like to coordinate
as to Friday. Shall we meet in front
of the halls at 7? We could go to Mønten
or maybe Blossom (unless you do not
care for smoke). A third option would be
Karrusellen (but the same deal as to smoke).
Looking forward to a pleasant
evening with you, regards Niels K

hi Niels

7 sounds fine

we'll decide prima vista

Stay out of trouble kids

we turn and look up

now don't be home too late!

August and Mai laugh and wave
they're leaning out of the kitchen window

sorry about that I say to Niels Klit

that's my best friend and her boyfriend
apparently they think we're enormously interesting

she was with you at the game he says

and I know August

from football

oh right I say and it occurs to me
they've seen each other naked

here you go

we're in Café Snork, Niels Klit
places two tall glasses in front of me

I hope you like wheat beer

he's hung his jacket over the back of his chair

on the breast pocket of his shirt it says *pocket*

it's a strange conversation

he gives me his full attention but
it's as though he doesn't get what I say

his voice is an exaggerated monotone

and even quieter than I remember

I have to lean across the table

mathematics is actually more about
forming an intuition

a what?

an intuition he says

than about memorising

what?

than memorising

mathematics is an abstract enterprise he says
people don't think about that very often

the greatest part of it exists only

up in our heads

We're back at halls at half past one

we wait for the lift

Niels Klit stands stock-still
I rock back and forth a bit on my feet

what?

I didn't say anything he says

all right. We wait a little longer

then he says in a loud voice

would you perhaps want to kiss?

I laugh without meaning to
he looks at me surprised

was that wrong of me to ask?

no I say. It just sounded funny

he nods for several seconds

but would you?

he kisses astonishingly well

I have to bend my head way back

after a couple of minutes I pull away
and place an index finger on his chest

does it also say *bike* on your bike?

When I step into the kitchen my heart skips a beat

shit, how come you're not asleep?

August sits on the bench with his legs up

I'm doing a cryptic crossword he says

at two in the morning?

someone had to make sure you got home safe

thanks Mum I say. What's a cryptic crossword?

grab a pew, he pats the seat
beside him, and I'll explain

I'm way too hungry I say and open the fridge

I could eat a horse

well so how'd it go?

we find some rye bread and sausage, and
August pops the caps off two beers with a fork

so are you two getting married?

it went well enough I say. He's tall

he's not your type

you don't know the first thing about him

I know him better than you do

so then why isn't he my type?

he's too boring

he's good at football I say

August looks at me

three plus four is seven he says
and cuts off a slice of cucumber

you can't be serious

mathematics is in fact a very abstract enterprise

I take a pull on my beer

the greatest part of it exists only

up in our heads

In the morning there's a cryptic crossword outside my door

I solve it in an hour and leave it in August's cupboard

impressive for a newbie

but what's a CIRQUE?

you can't make up your own words

                                        a kind of glacier

and SNAFFLE?

                                        part of a bridle

touché

August says you're good

Mai brushes crumbs from the duvet

at what?

at writing poems she says

we ate poppy-seed rolls for dinner and watched
three episodes of *Lost*. Now we're in her bed
leaning back against some large pillows

hello. He does

I try to not smile

okay I say

she tucks a lock of my hair behind my ear
it's so cosy having a sleepover

it is I say and pinch out a contact lens

when's his mum coming tomorrow?

Mai flops on her back

three thirty

Are you perchance Mai?

I meet his mum coming out of the lift

Mai and August have baked a raspberry tart and lit candles

over my dead body

his mother sits on the kitchen bench talking about
the catalogue text for her coming exhibition
she's displeased with the curator's draft

stilted and useless she says

hot air and pie in the sky

she's wearing an off-white silk blouse and has a jet-black bob

I stand at the counter and pretend
to leaf through a cookbook

Mai his mother says and crosses one leg over the other

do you ever go in to look at art?

Mum says August. Not really says Mai

no says his mother

because in this country art is for the few

ordinary people aren't allowed
to use it for anything whatsoever

she leans forward a little

and why is that?

Mum says August again

well among other things because of the way
we talk about art. Or the way that art

talks about *itself*

in ridiculous catalogue texts like this one for instance

that ought to *open* the works up

but close them off instead

because they're stuffed with pretentious
and self-serving bullshit

she snorts

then the cultural elite can stand there in the art museums
in utter silence, nobody daring to open their mouth
for fear of making a fool of themself

until afterwards in the darkness of some bar says his mother

then the knives come out

Mai stares at her entranced

August sits and dips a finger in wax

it's all a cliquish game of posturing says his mother
and sighs deeply, and I for one can't stand it

let us have a dialogue that is open and curious!

she's suddenly raised her voice

that is readily accessible!

that is for everyone!

it shouldn't be so difficult, she spreads her arms
you simply look at the work of art. Enter it. What do you see?

August slams a fist on the table

his mother does the same

and now my son thinks I should shut my mouth
she laughs and takes a sip of coffee

dear Mai, tell me a bit about yourself

I've heard so many good things about you

then Hannibal barges into the kitchen with two shopping
bags
he puts them down and wipes his hand on his trousers

Hannibal he says

Anna-Barbro

what?

Anna-Barbro she says, enunciating

this is my mother says August

hilarious

Hannibal starts to pull items out of the bags
I worry that he might start to fry something

the beer tally, the party snaps

I also feel embarrassed about our bulletin board
which his mother has a clear view of, and why hasn't Mai
poured the sour cream into a bowl?

but with regards to the opening says Anna-Barbro

I've told you I can't August interrupts

I'd like to go says Mai

if I may?

August glares at her

Hannibal stabs a knife into a package of cutlets

wonderful, Anna-Barbro claps her hands together
and then she invites Hannibal and me

what's your show actually about asks Mai

darkness says Anna-Barbro

I want her to say more

but she doesn't

want any more tart? August gets up

no thank you his mother says, it sits pretty heavy

she reaches down into her handbag
what's the deal again, sweetheart

is a person allowed to smoke?

That evening I google Anna-Barbro

*Anna-Barbro Oskarsson was born in 1965 and studied
at the Royal Danish Academy of Fine Arts. She created
the 26-foot-tall stair sculpture SONOS in Elsinore and
has had solo exhibitions at such museums as Trapholt
and KW Institute for Contemporary Art in Berlin.
She represented Denmark at the Venice Biennale
in 2008, and her works have been purchased by the
National Gallery of Denmark and MoMA in New York.*

I also find a description of the coming show:

*ROOM is a journey through eight rooms from twilight
to dawn, a site-specific installation that incorporates
both new and older sculptures, paintings, mobiles,
and other media. The exhibition culminates in the
sensational lightwork ROOM.*

the opening's Thursday at Kunsthal Charlottenborg

why didn't you tell me
your mother was a star

I dreamt about you last night

hello?

hello?

you're not answering
my question

and I also touched your eyes

they lay on Mai's nightstand

what was the dream?

Mai lies with her head in my lap

from just under the belly button to the edge
of his boxer shorts she says

that's probably my favourite part

or maybe his hands

she's holding her one arm in the air

they're so sexy. With those veins he has
don't you think his mother was nice?

yes I say and wonder
if nice is the right word

I think they look a lot like each other says Mai

especially the mouth, would you massage my scalp?

I unwind an elastic band from her hair

it's heavy and damp
and smells strongly of shampoo

we'll visit her when she's in Berlin this autumn
she has a big flat in Prenzlauer Berg

that sounds amazing I say

Mai smiles and closes her eyes

we'll have our own balcony

not so hard, Asta

what did you dream?

just answer

I'm not telling

it's boring to hear
other people's dreams

then why bring it up?

are you curious?

no

Could this be an arm asks Gregers

hmm, it's too big says Sif

we're doing a puzzle in the kitchen

I've been assigned the sky. It's impossible
all the pieces are blue. August sits there observing me

it's also very confusing

may I see? Linda leans across the table

that belongs to the sheep

it's a goat says Hannibal

I know someone by the way who can break
into our cable box, it'll cost a case of beer
he'll come by with a crowbar

I'm supposed to say hi from Niels Klit says August

now they're all looking at me

we can't really keep on
calling him Niels Klit says Mai
if Asta's going to be his girlfriend

why not?

August examines a puzzle piece

that *is* his name

I know a game we should play

a game?

K as in Katrine I say

O as in Ole says August

we sit across from each other on the kitchen bench
with paper and pencil, we're each supposed to make words
in twenty-five squares, we take turns saying a letter

L as in Leo I say

A he says and pauses

as in Asta

P I say and don't know where to look

as in potato

you were cutting up horses

                                        excuse me?

in my dream

you like waffles?

                                        yes

see you in the kitchen at 10

I accidentally throw my keys down the rubbish chute

They shouldn't be that hard to find

August has switched off the waffle iron and we've gone
down to the basement. There's a chill here. The chute empties out
into a wheelie bin behind a round hatch

it's got to be on top

he twists the handle

I leap back with a shriek

rubbish bags that were piled up in the chute explode outwards

a cascade of refuse

shit shouts August, brown liquid
spurting up onto his jeans, how disgusting!

it just keeps coming

bags flying out till they cover the entire floor

I've got tears in my eyes from laughing

we have to stand and catch our breath when the last one's landed

then we start from one end

your mum seems really cool I say, casting a bag to my right

and tiresome he says

and extremely dogmatic
careful there, that's got eggs

dogmatic how?

well about what makes a life worthwhile
I mean who threw this out, he studies
the blade from a bread knife. People are cuckoo

worthwhile in what way?

he sighs

if you're not pursuing art then you're just
a parasite that copulates and consumes and dies

I've heard that every day of my life he says

I'm getting pretty fed up with it
and she's a total hypocrite, yuck

he wipes his hand off on his jeans

everything you heard her say

about openings and the art scene
she's part of it herself you know. Stands there soaking it up
and letting everyone suck up to her, it's so fricking fake

it takes us over an hour to find the keys

it's impossible to stuff the bags back in the chute

what the hell were you thinking?

the caretaker's apoplectic, you think you're funny?

we laugh as he bawls us out

I sniff at my sleeve in the lift

I could use a shower I say

catharsis says August

I can hear him turn the water on

on the other side of the wall

it throbs in the pipes

We bike out to Assistens Cemetery with our hair wet

what I like about Copenhagen August says
and lets go of his handlebars, is how the graveyards
are also parks

we drink beer and eat waffles on the grass

that ran right through me

he gets to his feet. Don't look!

he goes to a bush and turns his back
I can hear the stream hit the ground

my thighs prickle, I have to stand up

and walk around a bit

then I place a palm on the saddle of his bike

it's hot from the sun, I feel dizzy

What'd you do today asks Mai

nothing special. I push back my chair

should I take your plate?

                                        want to play that
                                        letter game again

I'm with Mai

                                                    okay

                                                say hi

are you lonely
so be it!

                                            I'm not lonely

it's a quote, dummy

I thought you said
you read poetry

We step into Charlottenborg to thunderous applause

thank you says Anna-Barbro

thank you so much

she bows by a mic in the middle of the room
she's wearing a royal-blue jumpsuit, her dark hair set in back

she looks chic

diamantine

queenly

the ceiling here is high and the floor herringbone parquet

knots of people clutch wineglasses

God it's like an oven in here

Hannibal peels off his hoodie

Ollerup Boarding School

it says on the back of his T-shirt
I wish he'd don the hoodie again

then there's a buzz of conversation

should we go over and say hi?

Mai's voice is overeager
she's painted a thick black line around
each eye and bought a box of Merci chocolates

not right now

I glance at the people clustering around Anna-Barbro

she's busy I say

you think there's any grub?

Hannibal reverses his baseball cap, I'm starving

there's wine in any case I say, over there

have you guys come up with a theme for tour de chambre?

Mai takes a large swallow, we're on our second glass

I'm considering techno says Hannibal

didn't you do that last time?

that was an Ibiza theme he says and suppresses a yawn
it's just I've got a lot of glow sticks left over

Anna-Barbro's radiant

I keep an eye on her as we talk

she lays her hand on arms and shoulders
bubbles and beams, makes eyes and laughs

and all the time she's somewhere else

that's my distinct impression

she sits on some balcony behind her eyes
and observes, high above us all
and her pettability could give way in a flash to something

scourging

it doesn't make me like her any less

what about you, Asta?

Mai drains her glass, Anna-Barbro looks up
her gaze dwells on me a second or two
I just manage to lift my arm and wave

and then it drifts past. What?

you come up with a theme?

no I say and scratch my cheek, not yet

actually, do you have any more white wine?

Hannibal's emptied his glass and accosted
a woman in a white shirt who now calls across the room

Theis, are we out of Chablis?

there's a queue for the exhibition

it stretches all the way across the south wing

Anna-Barbro's created eight new spaces
laid out in a conch-like progression

that's what I hear a guy with a wide mouth say
he's got freckled arms and looks expectant

we're admitted in groups

hallo, guten Tag

Mai shakes hands with two German women
around sixty who are in our group

forward direction only says an attendant
otherwise you'll mess up the system

vorwärts, never backwards

even though it'll get dark in there he says
and then in English: very dark. Schwarz

the Germans nod

the one has a magenta scarf draped across
her shoulder, the other has glasses with invisible frames

and watch for the lights over the doorways he says
they turn white when you're supposed to move on

how exciting says Mai

it's just like a haunted house

the attendant looks at her

it's an art exhibition he says

it's already dim in the first room

eight wooden sculptures arranged in a circle

oblong with curved shapes
like giant alien limbs

the surfaces are covered in patterns
which take us some time to discover

ornamentation

a profusion of detail

these are so wild I say
and run a finger across the wood

the figures remind me of the tapestry in August's room
the sprouting vegetal creatures

the more intently I concentrate on them
the more they dissolve before my eyes

die Esel!

five richly coloured animal heads on plinths
in the second room, the German with the magenta scarf claps
her hands together, die habe ich in Frankfurt gesehen!

I don't think they look like donkeys

more like misshapen mythical beasts

bright and beautiful

lemon and bottle green
the glazes running together

lilac and orange

I wish I could see them in daylight

their teeth flash white in the dusk

as if they're laughing at us

I have a hard time tearing myself away but we've got to move on

the walls between the rooms
a sort of artwork as well

cement structures

installed side by side

with almost concealed doors, and over each one
a lamp no larger than a fingernail

when they light up they look like stars

the third room's empty
the darkness palpably thicker

spooky says Hannibal

then we notice the ceiling

it's covered in feathers, soft and billowy
like the coat of some animal. But the feathers
are constructed in paper

or so I gather from one of the Germans
who knows the work from before

they converse a good deal together about what they see
I translate in my head as best I can

what do you think she's really trying to do

Hannibal tips his head back

with all of this?

to explore the potential of darkness I say

something else I stole from the Germans

because all life comes out of darkness
foetuses and baby birds for example

and larvae when they pupate I say, seeds

six brass mobiles turn glinting
about themselves in the fourth room

they remind me of instruments

aeolian harps

being here fills me with joy

everything is itself and everything connects

in a special dream logic

there's a certain vitality to the pieces

a life energy, a drive

that's compelling and that
Anna-Barbro herself radiates

as if in these rooms I'm close to
something significant, an essence

a sort of marrow

that the darkness in some way amplifies

I observe Mai observing the harps
her face is dreamy too

unreal in the twilight

and suddenly I get an urge to
eat her, the whole exhibition

it's all so delicious and delectable

four landscapes in the fifth room

delicate and dissolving, ethereal
with faintly glowing horizons

a scent of citrus in the sixth

we're able to feel our way to a display case
but we can't see what's inside

we grow stiller and stiller

the Germans no longer speaking

I've lost all sense of time

shadows of shadows

in the seventh room it feels as though
something's circling around us, drifting

dancing

it dissipates when I turn towards it
only to materialise again, it's almost unsettling

the eighth room is pitch black

the walls here feel different

smooth and chill

it feels claustrophobic whispers Mai
I can smell her shampoo

how long are we going to be here?

shh, I fumble for her hand

we stand close together

waiting and waiting

then it starts to rain

light

leaping and glimmering droplets of light

and all at once thunder cracks overhead

from every side

we find ourselves in an elliptical room

the walls and ceiling one immense screen

a fireball, a blinding egg

we're encased in light

and in the midst of the light, a woman's voice

rising

impossible to descry
whether it's song or scream

I definitely liked the last room best

Hannibal struggles with his bike lock

the light show was super cool but it was
annoying that the rest was so dark

but that was the whole idea says Mai

Hannibal shrugs his shoulders, maybe
but you couldn't see the art

I hold my tongue

I don't feel like talking to anyone

I want to be by myself

something shuttles back and forth
between my brain and my chest

something joyful and quivery

I just think it was weird
she didn't come over and say hi

Mai kicks up her kickstand

I never even got to give her the chocolates

hey Asta, would you perhaps want
to drink some wine on the roof tonight?
I borrowed a key to the fire escape
and it's got a great view, regards Niels K

Wow says Sif

you look stunning!

I've put on lipstick and a knit top
that exposes my one shoulder

I've swung by the kitchen

she's got a date says Mai

she's leaning against August on the bench
he's wearing a white T-shirt and leafing through the paper

it isn't a date

I turn on the tap

with Niels Klit says Mai

the tall guy?

from the football team I say and
stick a finger under the stream

he's good-looking says Sif, what are you guys doing?

I fill a tumbler and tell her about the roof

August doesn't look up

The sky's pastel and vast

oh!

I tip back my head

I thought you'd like it
says Niels Klit, looking happy

we sit down behind a small screen

he's brought a quilt and some large cushions
pistachios and a cooler bag for the wine
plus two real glasses rolled up in dishtowels

you've gone all out I say

but of course he says

he's wearing shorts and sits cross-legged
his knees are smooth and pale brown

the sun declines overhead

fire and gold

like sitting on a film set or
in the midst of a masterpiece as it's being painted

the exhibition has sharpened my senses

altered them

everything's heightened and significant

charged with beauty and possibility

the glowing sky
the taste of pistachios

Niels Klit's knees

I study them intently

they're almost unbearably beautiful

I lean forward a little

so here's where you're sitting and smooching

Mai suddenly stands in the staircase door
August emerges laughing behind her

this really wasn't my idea

she bends over and kisses my cheek
Niels Klit gets hair in his face

but it's going to be so nice

a sort of double date, can you spare a bit of cushion?

where'd you get a key I ask
and sweep together the pistachio shells

I have my methods says August
he pulls a six-pack of Harboes out of a rucksack
and there's more where these came from

he nudges the cooler bag with his foot

if you get tired of wine

it's insane says Mai

with the stars

the four of us are lying on our backs

it's midnight now and very dark up here

she's borrowed August's sweatshirt and lit a cigarette
he's resting the back of his head in his hands, Niels Klit
lies on my other side and strokes my thigh
tentatively with his thumb

and the moon says Mai

I mean just look at it!

Niels Klit clears his throat

there are some scientists he says, who have started
to develop a very special sphere

that'll be the world's roundest object

Mai leans over towards him
can't you speak a little louder?

a very special sphere I say

of pure silicon says Niels Klit

that will be the actual definition of a kilogram

because the cylinder we've based our definition on
up till now has lost fifty micrograms

due to molecular displacement

he clears his throat again

and that's a huge problem

you can't of course have a constant
that's based on a variable

what?

you can't have a constant I say

that's based on a variable

I don't understand says Mai

it *is* kind of complicated says Niels Klit

I don't think so says August
I think it's quite simple

Mai sits up

I've really got to pee

she grinds a butt into a beer can
I don't suppose there's a toilet up here

Niels Klit gets to his feet
you can go down with me and use mine

August and I are left lying there

we don't speak

we watch a plane blink across the sky

well he says

but I also know something that you don't

what's that?

you can't write with a ballpoint pen in space

I see

because it's Earth's gravity
that draws the ink out

intriguing I say, you're so bright

he turns on his side

you're looking in the wrong direction I say
you're supposed to look up. At the fascinating firmament
let yourself be ravished by the infinite

he doesn't respond, only smiles

look up!

I try to sound stern

just stop it, August
you're so irritating

why are you looking at me?

he laughs and I poke him on the shoulder

look up!

I try to turn his head
he takes hold of my wrist

then we hear Mai's voice
and the door to the roof opens

I can't fall asleep

what's joyful and quivery has shifted

it's slid further down in my body
and presses against my pelvic floor

I toss and turn

In the middle of the night I get a text

it's from August

you asleep?

Don't

I tell myself
three times in the darkness

don't

don't

Hey what is with you this morning?

I'm just giving you a hug I tell Mai
why don't we hang out and have fun today?

because I've got work she laughs

I run into August down in the laundry room

he's pulling clothes from the dryer
when I enter, and it makes us both jump

good morning he says

it's almost noon I say and walk past him with my basket

he runs a hand through his hair

should I show you how they work?

I've been down here before I say
and open the lid. Even though that's not true

I've put off my laundry till now

okay, he says, the system's just a bit tricky

I fill the drum, I can feel his gaze

then he starts to fold his socks

he's got a special technique I see out of the corner of my eye
the socks become squares

it's hot and humid down here

almost like a sauna

I start to hum

it's totally stupid
but now I have to keep going

he shakes a black sock

so did you see my text last night?

no I say and bang down the lid

because I was sleeping

like a normal person and I think
it's not okay to text people so late
you could have woken me up or something

in fact it shows a lack of respect

did you have to get up early then?

it's the principle of the thing, August

and why are you standing there waiting for me
can't you just go up to the kitchen?

I'm not waiting for you

he resumes making his squares

these things won't fold themselves you know

I look at him

you're so provoking I say

then I turn back to the machine

there are so many different buttons

after a while he says

the little one on the left has to be pushed all the way in

We stand close in the lift

I can smell his dried clothes

and cologne

it's woody, with a whiff of alcohol

I'm not sure I like it

I can see us in the mirrors

from every side simultaneously

the light stutters

it's been that way forever he says

I move my foot a little

he clears his throat

there's something I'd like to ask you

well I say and pick some lint from my sleeve

ask away

he smiles

how many priests does it take to change a light bulb?

Holy mother of God

the driver struggles with my suitcase

did you dismember a horse or something?

nah I say. It's just books

I'm doing a writing residency on Lolland
the retreat's in a wooded part of the island
it doesn't register on the cab's GPS

that's really strange

the driver takes a sip of flat coke
we've driven in circles for twenty minutes
looking for a purple mailbox

the cab smells of French fries

this is like the Bermuda Triangle he says

then he swats the steering wheel, down there for Christ's sake!

so you found it then

the owner of the retreat's called Sanne Sax Mortensen
she stands on the gravel with outspread arms
her hair long and honey-coloured

it's hard to tell how old she is

let me take that

it's really heavy I say

she brushes me aside

hush my dear

she glides effortlessly up the stairs

her hair billowing behind her
they must be extensions

the house is old and smells clean

spritzed in lavender

I got to everything but the mirrors says Sanne
but now you'll get a tour

she's a clairvoyant and holds sessions behind a red door

the rest is run as an artists' retreat
it used to be a holiday camp for kids
for an entire century she says

and points to a litter box

there are also three Siamese kittens in residence
but they live their own lives

dangling crystals

lots of scatter cushions and blankets

each room is colour-coordinated and full of knickknacks

I'm to stay in the attic room in an orgy of orange

you need to push hard on the handle says Sanne
and the floor can be cold on the feet and those are local
she points to a bowl of strawberries. The Wi-Fi code
is kittycat and now love, I'll leave you in peace

the garden is bursting with green

I slide the desk over in front of the window

a kitten lurks under a bush and peers up at me

I wish you could hear me

on the windowsill stands a cast of an old-fashioned phone

with words across the receiver in flowing golden script

having fun on Lolland?

fun and fun

I'm writing

anyone there besides you?

a Japanese artist couple
in the double room

Yoshi and Hiromi

a sculptor with a beard
he's usually down in the studio

Jonas something or other

a young guy just started in property management

Janus

very cocky, he just
gave me two tickets

to Erotic World at Valby Hall

just came and put them on my desk

It turns out the sculptor's name isn't Jonas but Jonatan

and he's not a sculptor

but usually works in pencil and ink
it's only now that he's started to experiment
with three dimensions

would you like one?

he stands in the kitchen boiling an entire box of eggs

he smells of campfire, he's been firing raku
in an oil barrel all morning

and it's been going pear-shaped he laughs

we bear coffee and eggs out onto the terrace

they're perfectly what is called smiling
halfway between hard and soft

such a relief he says
I'm not completely devoid of talent

he's got a broad mouth and freckles on his arms

he eats five with salt and pepper

then he fiddles a bit with his phone
dead as a doornail since I got here he says
and puts it back in his pocket

but I suppose it's good for the art

so Asta

why don't you tell me a bit about your book?

hmm I say. I'd rather not

I get you, he says, don't jinx it

it's all about not stressing the clay

he initiates me instead into what he knows
about raku, speaking with enthusiasm
about temperatures and time, about crazing

I clear my throat

are you familiar perhaps with Lysander Milo?

hell yeah says Jonatan

I saw his busts last winter and was blown away

they're incredible. In fact they were what made
me want to work in some new media
to try my hand at whatever I could

you know how you see something and think: that!

that's so beautiful and pure, I want to do that too

his laugh is loud, and then
you discover how hard it is

he overturns an eggshell

if it looks unbelievably simple he says

it's frightfully complicated to create

it's just that people don't always understand that

I thought I was going to write a book about Lysander Milo I
say

exciting says Jonatan

but you're not going to after all?

no I say and wave to Yoshi and Hiromi
who are walking past down in the garden. Definitely not

they study flowers and plants each morning
they're given to laughter and they're nearly the same height

they wave back

he plays the flute says Jonatan

I can hear it through my wall

it's insanely beautiful

I wake early to a quiet house

two of the kittens lie outside my door

I fondle them between the ears
they follow me down to the kitchen

I make coffee, drink it at the table in solitude

it's good and strong

a dream catcher hangs before the window

and on the wall a calendar
I didn't notice before

I push back my chair

the calendar's a riot of flowers

IUNIE IULIE

the months are spelled oddly

AUGUST SEPTEMBRIE

I leaf back and forth
the cats rub up against my legs

MAI

it doesn't say a year

What kind of calendar is that?

I ask Sanne that afternoon
she's scouring the kitchen sink in a kimono
and yellow rubber gloves
her long hair is plaited and pinned up

it's a perpetual calendar she says

that I bought in Romania once

a thousand years ago

I thought it looked romantic
what about it?

nothing I say. Is it Romanian?

I should think so, love

may I borrow it for a while?

she rubs a forearm against her forehead

you bet she says, but can I ask you a favour?
can I get you to push up my right sleeve?

I sit down in my room with the calendar

Later I take a walk along the paths through the woods

I have an idea for something in my novel
that I need to think through

a key perhaps

I don't meet a soul

what's so funny?

Jonatan looks up when I return

he's sitting on the terrace with the paper
and tapping his foot in a green felt slipper
there's a pair of the same kind in my room but orange

is your room green I ask

completely he says, you want some coffee?

what first got you started with drawing?

we've moved our chairs out into the sun
Jonatan rests his head against the back of his chair

it's a while before he answers

it was a space I could go into and disappear

if that makes any sense he says

I nod and take a sip of coffee
it does I say. And who do you like?

I mean artists

all sorts he says

Anna-Barbro Oskarsson for example, hey

he straightens up and thumps me on the back

there's something whimsical about her pieces, just
cough it out, Asta. Or inviting

they point to her approach

it's hard to explain, should I get you some water?

it's fine I say and get my voice under control

you feel like she must have had a blast says Jonatan

you know her?

I've heard the name I say

it's a long time since she's had any shows

he opens a carton of milk
she lost her son some years ago

ten maybe, can you grab the sugar?

and then she moved to Berlin. Thanks. But this autumn
apparently there's some amazing news

I turn to face him

about Anna-Barbro?

yes he says

at Charlottenborg

a huge comeback, a kind of rebirth

her last exhibition was also there
it had to do with darkness. I saw it three times he says
went to the opening and everything

I don't know much about the new show

it's in October I think, he takes a sip

or maybe November

aren't *you* having fun

Sanne steps out onto the terrace with a large stack
of solid-colour blankets, now that I've got you here she says

and shakes a bright pink one out over the railing

I'm thinking about having a little dinner party
out here tomorrow, she neatly folds the blanket

nothing fancy, just so we can look each other in the eye

raise a glass

you *are* leaving soon, Asta

when are you coming home?

Friday

sorry I haven't been
very responsive

can you watch Bertram then?

there's a summer party for the City offices
feels like I haven't danced in years

of course

you're a peach

we're all born
without kneecaps

says who?

so that it doesn't hurt to crawl

I dreamed last night that we were 43

and I simply couldn't understand it
because we'd just been 33

Sanne wants to make a lamb dish

a bit of a girls' day out

she invites me to go with her to Maribo to buy groceries

she rides the accelerator
and keeps gesturing as she drives
her hands hardly touch the wheel

my legs are shaking when we get out in front of SuperBrugsen

mozzarella, Asta

she strides down the aisles
and hustles me through the store

I've never shopped so efficiently

in five minutes we've found everything

and then this and a pack of Prince Lights

she places a striped blanket on the conveyor belt

she gazes intently at the boy behind the till as we pay

he lost someone recently she says and
slams the car door, I'd bet both my arms
on it, there was someone at any rate who
wanted to tell him something, no question about it

she sighs and turns the key

it's not really something I can switch on and off

They're usually so timid says Sanne

we're unpacking the groceries and
a kitten rubs up against my leg
they've begun to follow me
around the house, to jump up on my lap

they're sweet I say and pick it up

I'm in a good mood, something's clicked with my manuscript

and thanks for letting me borrow that calendar by the way

anytime says Sanne, no you know what?

she walks across the floor

I think in fact that there's some
leftover veal stock, she opens the freezer. Hmm

and that it's hiding somewhere in here

I had another writer living here in April
and she made food as if her life depended on it

pot roast and turkey drumsticks and anything you could
think of

and then she'd sit out there and eat
on the steps, all by herself. Bingo!

she fishes out a freezer bag

but people are strange

I also had this printmaker in the attic once
who I didn't see hide nor hair of for two weeks

she shakes her head

he had his demons that man
let me tell you. He brought
so much darkness with him, it hung over the whole house

and the morning he left she says

I found this pattern of spruce needles on the floor of his room
incredibly intricate. It must've taken him all night

that was in December, she brightens up

I always buy an enormous tree
you have to promise to come at Christmas someday

the lamb stew's a success

golden and flavourful

we toast and toast in the evening sun

it's all very lovely

like we eating heaven says Yoshi

his English is poor, Hiromi has to translate
most things for him. I like hearing them
speak together in Japanese, they're full
of solicitude for each other

I can tell without understanding the words

I'll probably never see them again
it suddenly occurs to me

I get tears in my eyes

then Jonatan puts down his cutlery

what's up with the bricks

he pushes back his chair

is there some decoration on them?

they're inscribed says Sanne

with names. She points. Of all the children
who stayed in this house through the years
didn't any of you notice?

I stand next to Jonatan

the wall is covered with names and years

scratched into the brick

in sundry hands

so many that they swim before my eyes

we eat nougat ice cream and discuss the symbolism of names

Jonatan means blue moon in Japanese
my name means a thousand roots

Sanne's means nothing

that really gets us laughing

we light candles and Yoshi fetches his flute

he plays for a long time

everything's so beautiful that it's almost too much

shall I grab you a blanket?

Sanne and I are the last ones left

yes please I say. Mostly to make her happy

the two of us can manage one more glass
she's got a bottle of white under her arm

the night is starry and very still

I caress a kitten. Sanne lights a cigarette

we sit for a while and gaze into the darkness

do you have any kids?

no she says and wafts the smoke away
I always knew I wouldn't

deep in my soul

she crosses one leg over the other
I had my tubes tied when I was twenty-seven

boom

she lets the sandal slip from her foot. It was a big relief
then I didn't have to worry about it anymore

she sits considering her toes

her face looks young in the candlelight

what about you, ducks? Do you want children?

yes I say

she nods

actually very much so

is that why you're sad?

I'm not sad

yes you are she laughs. At first I thought
it was unrequited love, she regards me

but apparently not

you just have a very powerful middle field

that's what confused me

I let my fingers slide through the fur
I don't know what to say

I have the sense of relinquishing a grip

of falling

floating in the air

it's not unpleasant

Sanne inhales deeply and looks out across the yard

when I turned forty-one she says
I fell in love with a man
who was thirty years older

he left the wife he'd lived with for so long

and moved in down here

we had five very happy years together

beautiful years. Then he began
to turn his gaze towards death

in what way I ask

is he still alive?

he moved back in with her

Sanne stubs out her cigarette

moved home, she smiles briefly

it was meant to be

I visit them both once in a while
we drink coffee and talk about books and art

my clients, their daughter

they're old now

Sanne clears her throat and smooths the tablecloth

then she looks at me with gentle eyes

I'm not sure what that has to do with anything

she gives my hand a squeeze

but here we sit

I wake in the middle of the night with a start

there's a knock on my door

hello?

I sit up in the bed

Sanne?

I turn on the light

now it's totally quiet

I place a hand on my chest
it was a dream, it was a dream
my heart slowly settles down

then another knock

I jump out of bed
cross the floor, hesitate a moment

and throw open the door

there's nobody there

I return from Lolland in a foul mood

I open all the windows in the flat
I print out three hundred and twenty-six pages
and set up an appointment

at the Copenhagen Fertility Centre

then I lie down on the sofa and stare at the ceiling

there's a through-draught

my suitcase is still standing in the middle of the floor

I take a deep breath on Mai's front step. Then I ring the bell

What is it?

she's put mascara on one eye and her hair's up
in a turban, the flat smells of Red Door

something you have to read

is it your book?

yes. Wait!

I place my hand on the envelope

not until tomorrow

when I'm not here

okay, I'm actually in a rush
Bertram! she yells into the living room
but my God I'm so thrilled

can you hear who's here she yells

he hasn't talked about anything else

small footfalls

I crouch down

hey what is it with you asks Mai half an hour later

I'm just giving you a hug I say
all of a sudden I just don't want you to leave

I'm coming back you know

she laughs and kisses me on the cheek
am I wearing too much blush?

no I say and hoist Bertram on my hip

you look nice

we make food in his play kitchen

he serves a long series of invisible dishes

we build a carport under the dining table
and read a picture book about a toolbox
that comes to life, he giggles and giggles
when I do the fretsaw's voice

he's bright and happy

the entire time I'm on the cusp of tears

I feel as if I'll never see him again

he falls asleep leaning against me on the sofa

I switch off Peppa Pig

the living room's quiet

the envelope for Mai rests on the dresser

a bomb, a carnivorous plant

how did I ever persuade myself
to bring it here? My heart races

I consider throwing it out the window

Bertram emits a little sigh

I look at his face

his eyelids quiver

they glisten like mother-of-pearl

I have an urge to lick them

his cheeks are smooth and chubby

something rises up through my body

hot and savage

with furious speed

I'm suddenly scared I'll come
to sink my teeth into them, bite off a hunk
crush him with my entire weight

tear him to pieces, scream

explode

then he starts expanding in my arms

the spine grows longer, the hands broader
the skull creaks and yields, the nose pushes out

his breathing makes me faint

he grows heavy

I feel his heart through the skin
of my chest, a huge muscle

my vision goes dark

the phone flashes on the coffee table

hello I whisper

hi says Mai, loud music and voices
in the background, how are you guys doing?

we're good I say and clear my throat

oh that's great she says with relief

I have no idea what it was
yes please she tells someone

but without the cucumber and black pepper!

I just had this feeling that
something terrible was about to happen

she laughs, I know it's silly

I try to laugh too but
all that comes out is a little sound

is it a fun party?

yes she says

but I miss you guys. Is he sleeping?

like a rock

I wake up at three fifteen

Mai must have come home

borne Bertram to bed
and covered me with a quilt

the envelope on the dresser's gone

something churns within me

I love you

I write on a napkin
and slip down the staircase

it's starting to grow light

not a breeze, the first birds

I feel nauseous all day

I check my phone constantly

at six I call Mai

she doesn't pick up

will you answer your phone?

please, Mai

I can't endure this

I lie awake all night

In the morning I go to her place

she doesn't answer the intercom

I walk through the gate and back to the courtyard

Bertram's pram is gone

The building's taller than I remember

I stand outside a long time looking up

you going in?

three young people are coming out
the guy holds the door open for me

no thanks

such a gentleman

one of the girls ruffles his hair

and always attentive he says

she laughs and zips up her jacket
they disappear down the avenue

I regret it. The door's locked

I press my forehead against the glass façade

I wait a while for someone to appear

but no one does

you're on private property

the caretaker's bent over a grill
on the other side of the building
he's scouring the grate with a steel brush

his hair's grown thin

sorry I say

it's just because I used to live here

so have a lot of people

he scrubs a bit harder

and still nobody's learned
to clean up after themselves, he straightens up
and looks at me accusingly

unless of course you think
it's just jolly to have rats
crawling around on the grates at night?

umm no I say

but I was actually wondering if you perhaps
would be so kind as to let me in?

he knits his brows

I won't touch a thing I say
I just want to be in there for a couple minutes

be in there for a couple minutes?

yes

he points the brush at me
I'm sure he's about to start shouting

then he sighs and tosses his head

it's open over there he says

there's an odd light in the lobby

watery and transparent

nobody else

I close my eyes, take a deep breath

the lift rumbles

Asta!

Hannibal has four heads of cabbage in his arms
he holds the door open with his foot

you going up?

tonight's the tour de chambre
everyone on the floor has to have a theme
we'll visit each of the rooms in turn

fuck

he drops a head when we step out onto fifth
and it rolls down the corridor. I pick it up

what are they for?

wouldn't you like to know

the entire floor's in a frenzy
everyone busy with their preparations

welcome to reception

my theme is the first day of school

I've made a banner from an old bedsheet
I blow up balloons and I've bought half pints of milk
that I'll spike with vodka and Kahlua

what are you looking at?

Mai and I are drinking afternoon coffee

I've spotted August below, he's cycling
across the parking lot with his jacket unzipped
I haven't seen him since the laundry room

nothing I say, are you ready for tonight?

my body feels terribly restless

I listen to loud music in my room, swing
my arms in circles and run a long time in place

yet it doesn't help

we meet in the kitchen at six o'clock

the idea is to lay down a solid foundation

Sif's seen to dinner

goulash and mashed potatoes

we drink Asti in plastic glasses

almost a feeling of New Year's

Hannibal glances about

are we missing anyone?

August says Mai

and with that he shows up
he's painted on a black moustache

sorry he says, just had to take care of one last detail

Mai cups her hands around his face
my you look old she laughs

you look like you're thirty

ugh the saltwater theme says Sif as we eat

you guys remember that?

how do you do a saltwater theme I ask

it's hard to get the food down

I sit with a lump of mashed potato in my cheek
and focus on not looking at August

eye contact feels perilous

you don't says Gregers
we had this exchange student from Lithuania
it was really poorly executed

but the most hopeless theme ever
Hannibal says and starts to chortle

the land surveyor theme!

now we're all laughing

it was the guy who lived in your room says Linda
he was so gross, his name was Bjarke
and he kept his milk products at room temperature

you're much more hygienic

oops sorry

August knocks over my wineglass

now I'm forced to meet his gaze

he grins broadly

I'm almost certain it was on purpose

everyone's in stitches from the story of the time
a resident named Rose found a doughnut hole
on the beak of her stuffed eagle

she did a Christmas theme explains Hannibal
and studied veterinary science, it was totally dried out

I do feel like it was a falcon says Linda

your full attention, people!

Sif positions herself at the end of the table
we have to draw lots for the order

is it best to be at the end or the beginning?

depends on your theme says Mai

once they never made it farther than Kim's room
because he served absinthe and devised
a rebus-based treasure hunt inspired by Heidegger

what kind of theme was that?

a continental philosophy theme says Kim

we draw slips of paper from Hannibal's cap

Mai will be first, I'll be last

in fact that's a relief, then I can
see how the others do it

how come you haven't eaten anything?

August leans across my plate

but I have

he sticks his fork into a piece of beef

hey I say, that's mine

he puts it in his mouth, he chews and smiles

what are you going to do about it?

then the kitchen phone rings, it's Mai

we're invited to come now

dear children of God

she stands before her door with outspread arms

she's dressed in a black bin liner
and a minister's ruff folded out of paper

welcome to my church!

she's lit pillar candles and lowered the blinds

so now shall I ask of thee

she's asked August and Gregers to kneel before her
they're to be wed, the ceremony drags out
because she keeps dissolving in laughter

August Oskarsson

she says in an unctuous voice

do you take, she clears her throat

loses it then completely

I sure as hell do says August and gets up
I take everything, he places a hand upon
Gregers's nape. Looks him in the eye

and then presses his tongue in his mouth

everyone whoops and claps

and now Gregers kisses him back

tentatively at first. Then tenderly and deep

a nerve quivers in my thigh

this is the body of Christ

there isn't supposed to be Communion at a wedding says Linda

it is I who am the minister

Mai dispenses vanilla wafers. So it is I
who decide. Eat little piggies

and salty liquorice shots from a tray

this is the blood of Christ

then she puts on Toxic

hocus pocus filiocus says Kim

we sit in the window while the others dance
it comes from the sacrament, did you know that?

I'm drinking my beer, August grasps Mai by the waist

what do you mean sacrament

when the bread and the wine are transubstantiated he says

hoc est corpus filii, it's magic
or really, it's Latin

but in point of fact we're eating Christ he says

it's even wilder than intercourse

love and cannibalism

Kim, August shouts

you talk too much, we're going to your room!

Kim's theme is time

he's wearing two wristwatches and serves
a concoction of green tea, cognac, and calvados

and you shouldn't be able to see anything!

the idea is to calculate how long
a minute lasts, we sit around in a circle
with blindfolds on. Hannibal loses big time

Sif is runner-up

I'm only one second off nailing it exactly

the prize is a large Toblerone

it doesn't really fit the theme says Kim
it was just something I had lying around

congrats says August and punches me on the shoulder

every time I look at him
he's already looking at me

we need to move on

Mai dances down the corridor

Gregers is drunk as a skunk

AVANT-GARDE CABBAGE

there's a sign over the door to Hannibal's room

an avant-gardistic
avant-garde exhibition

he's got an orange towel slung across
his shoulders and he hands us wineglasses from a tray

Chablis he says in an affected voice

I take a sip

but it's straight vodka

we're to create a work of art in pairs
with one of us serving as the other's arms

me and Asta!

August leaps to my side

we have twenty glow sticks and a cabbage at our disposal

ready steady go yells Hannibal and flings
his towel with exaggerated fervour

maybe it'd be easier says August
and grasps my hands
if you sort of lock them behind me

like so

I intertwine my fingers behind his lower back

I feel a ticklish jolt in my groin

we try to make a porcupine
but it's an utter debacle

Linda and Kim are the clear winners
with an astonishingly beautiful piece

they've wedged glow sticks beneath the cabbage leaves

the head luminesces

boys and girls, August bows before us

he has a casino theme

he's scattered playing cards across the floor
and serves vermouth in a button-up shirt and suspenders

and now I'm going to ask for total silence!

Russian roulette

we stand in a circle with cans of beer
they've been doled out at random and one's been pre-shaken

the moment of truth says Hannibal

we count down from ten

and then foam spurts up in his face
we hoot and howl
he lifts the beer in the air like a trophy

Mai licks my ear, Linda makes out
with Sif, Kim and Gregers open a window

and bellow into the night

and I realise that some dissolution is underway

rapidly escalating

I feel curiously sober

hands down they're humping says Hannibal

Mai and August have disappeared when it's time to move on

I'll find them I say

Mai? I knock on her door

the pillar candles are still burning, I blow them out

they're not in his room either

they're out in the kitchen

kissing passionately on a chair
Mai athwart August

sorry I say and he tips her off

I don't mean to disrupt
it's just that we're going to Linda's now

Linda's too gone to explain the theme
but no one cares anymore anyhow

recycling maybe or green energy

she sends around a bottle of tequila
and asks us to trade clothes, we hop around
from person to person, pulling on sleeves and trouser legs

August has a beauty mark above his belly button

I laugh uproariously at something I didn't catch

you're drowning says Hannibal
I've commandeered his hockey jersey
it's navy blue and way too big

it says 33 in white on my back

how you doing out there, RO! SKIL! DE!

Sif's set up two igloo tents in her room

a beer bong with a yellow gas can

music festival theme

I wipe the foam from my mouth
and crawl into the rear one
I need to be alone

press pause

regain control of something in my head and my body

someone turns up the music

I lie down and shut my eyes

hi!

August's suddenly on his way into the tent

he's donned Mai's dress
and combed back his hair

hi I say and sit up

you look like your mum

he laughs and zips up the flap

no I say. You've got to stop

stop what?

he turns back around
we look at each other

what am I doing?

stop it, August

then I lean forward
and kiss him with eyes wide open
unzip the flap and tumble out

in one fluid motion

the others are all entangled on Sif's double bed

I fling myself among them

Kim puts a leg across my thigh, Mai bites
me on the arm, I bore my nose into her hair
and now August topples onto the bed too

he's heavy and warm

Mai kisses him on the neck
he fumbles for my hand

I intertwine my fingers with his

our hands grip each other tight

and I think for a fleeting happy moment
that it's all lovely and good and immaterial
because all of us are one

then Gregers vomits in a rubber boot

first a thin clear stream
and then out in the corridor

great gushes of goulash

and I know that we won't go any farther
that it'll all disintegrate now

get me a broomstick!

Mai wants to do the limbo, Kim and Sif sing Queen
August and I careen around with Gregers
who can't keep his feet

got him?

giddyap!

Mai leaps onto Hannibal's back
a broomstick she yells, I'm the limbo king
they canter away towards the storeroom
she's laughing and bobbing up and down

how can one body be so heavy I gasp

you think he needs his stomach pumped?

thanks for everything sniffs Gregers
his breath smells of ammonia

you've been a good wife

thank *you* my friend says August
and to me: not at all. Careful
there's a pool of puke there!

we topple Gregers onto his bed
August struggles with his shoes

I glance around the room

it's extremely tidy

horror theme I say and point to the desk

bloody Marys and a pair of fangs

a skeleton costume hangs ready over a chairback

Gregers looks younger than usual

his sleeping face completely open
we regard him awhile

we're standing close to each other

then August wraps his arm around me
I fear I'm going to faint

a grunt from the bed, neither of us laugh

August twists his head around in the semidarkness

I slip from his arm
and stuff the fangs in my mouth

you thuppothe they'll thine in the dark?

the fangs are huge, I lisp and drool

August laughs at me

I don't know he says

but we can test them. Come!

it's cramped in the bathroom

brace yourself, he's still laughing
and has a finger on the switch

I shove the teeth into place

Asta Basta he says. Are you ready?

I can smell his skin

my fangs glow

then they're lying in the sink

his mouth is warm

we stand there a long time in the dark

someone fumbles with the handle

Gregers flings open the door and lurches towards the toilet
we tumble out into the corridor and start to laugh

August has to place his hands on his knees

I'm sobbing

slowly we catch our breath

then he straightens up and looks into my eyes
his cheeks ablaze and his hair tousled

he's radiant

you make me happy he says

something lifts in my chest
and leaps out, explodes

if that's okay

I come to laugh again

then I nod and smile

it's okay I say

let's go to your room says August eagerly

I want to see your theme

he sets into a run

you go ahead, I'm just going to get some beers!

I need to just stand there a moment

my body atingle

I have the sense that each of my limbs
would float off in a different direction
if I moved the least little bit

I close my eyes

was that a sound?

I open them again

I can hear somebody banging

in the distance. On a door

they don't let up

I take a couple of steps

now someone's shouting too

I stop, listen

resume

the sounds come from the storeroom

let us out!

it's Hannibal. And Mai

louder shouts, a hammering

I stand before the door

then turn around and sprint to my room
sit in the window. Wait

an eternity

then the kitchen door slams

rapid steps heading this way

all of a sudden I run over and turn the key

Asta?

a second later August knocks

I hold my breath

he grasps the knob

are you asleep?

silence

you're not asleep he says
I don't believe that

he knocks again

what's going on, Asta?

his voice is very gentle

we don't have to drink these beers
I hear him set them down

I'm actually not that drunk he says

in case you'd like to know

I know you're there

more silence

I've never felt that way before he says then

felt this

there's a prickling behind my eyelids
I open and clench my fists

this feeling he says
in my body. And in my brain

whenever I'm near you

then he clears his throat. Okay

I'm going to go sit in the kitchen, Asta

I'll wait for you out there, deal?

so I'm going now

he remains standing there

knocks one more time

and then he leaves

I lean against the door for a while

then I crawl into my bed with all my clothes on

I'm shaking

I want to disappear

I wake to running footsteps and screams out in the corridor

the morning light streaming into my room

stop calling

we're on our way to see the draught horses

in case you'd like to know

I run the whole way

I see Mai before she sees me

she's sitting on the curb
the pram's beneath a tree

she turns her head. I halt

then she gets up

I wanted to show him the horses

she stares at me

now that I just read about them

Mai I say

but it's closed, she takes a step forward

you're a psychopath she says

because you didn't tell me about this

what the hell were you thinking?

did you think I'm too weak? That I can't take it?

you think I'd get angry with you or
have a nervous breakdown? That was ten years ago!
you think I can't understand your feelings
but everyone's got the same bleeding heart!

you think you're smarter than me

and stronger than me

you think you're better than anyone else

you're so thick in the head, Asta, you really are

you think you can manage everything yourself
that you don't need to tell anyone how you're doing

that your longings are unique

that you're so fucking special that nobody can
ever really reach you or help you with anything

it's conceited and arrogant

I'm your best friend

I'm right here. Forever

get that through your head!

and you can write whatever the hell you want

about me, about Bertram. You can use all of it

but you need to let me in

yeah. Go ahead and cry but

it's about time

That business about the fertility clinic she says

is that true?

we've walked over to West Cemetery
Bertram's asleep, the sun is shining

yeah

when is it?

on Tuesday. Before Blossom

okay she says

I'll go with you

we walk awhile without speaking

I went out to the halls I say
should we sit down for a bit?

we've found a bench by a pond
Mai parks the pram

this morning before you texted

why?

I don't know I say

just because

I was there yesterday, she sits down
beside me and opens her jacket

you were?

she shrugs

yeah but only down on the street
ah look how beautiful

she points

the light over there, like gold

or because I felt a connection I say

a pull

and then afterwards grief. An idiotic grief

after all I hardly got to know him

Mai doesn't speak

I'm lonely I say
so awfully lonely

sorry Mai

she closes her eyes
and tilts her face to the sun
breathes calmly

there's something I didn't tell you

what?

Janus kissed me

I turn to face her

what do you mean, from property management?

at the summer party she says

Bertram makes a noise

that's so bloody marvellous I say

she gets up

he's twenty-four, Asta

she fusses with the folding top, I mean good grief
her whole face is beaming

such a little rascal

there's absolutely no way I can work with that

you asleep?

no

I think we should have different names

you and me

like what?

you should be something with an A

Anna

or Asta

what do you want to be called?

you decide

ACKNOWLEDGEMENTS

The lines 'are you lonely / so be it!' on p. 223 are from Gunnar Ekelöf 'Untitled' in *Selected Poems*, translated from the Swedish by WH Auden & Leif Sjöberg, Penguin, 1971.

BIOGRAPHIES

TINE HØEG (b. 1985) is a Danish author. Her novel *New Passengers*, published by Lolli Editions in 2020, won an English PEN Award and Bogforum's Debutantpris, the prize awarded each year for the best literary debut published in Denmark. Høeg's own adaptation of the novel has been staged at the Royal Danish Theatre. She lives in Copenhagen.

MISHA HOEKSTRA has translated numerous Danish authors, including Hans Christian Andersen and Maren Uthaug. In 2017, he received the Danish Translation Prize, and his translation of Dorthe Nors's *Mirror, Shoulder, Signal* was shortlisted for the International Booker Prize.

Memorial, 29 June
Copyright © Tine Høeg, 2020
Originally published in Danish as *Tour de chambre* by Gutkind, Copenhagen
Translation copyright © Misha Hoekstra, 2023
This English-language edition first published in the United Kingdom
by Lolli Editions in 2023

The right of Tine Høeg to be identified as the author of this work has
been asserted in accordance with Section 77 of the Copyright, Designs
and Patents Act 1988

Memorial, 29 June is No. 12 in the series New Scandinavian Literature

Graphic design by Kasper Vang
Printed and bound by TJ Books Limited, United Kingdom, 2023

This translation was made possible through the generous support
of the Danish Arts Foundation, the Fondation Jan Michalski, and
Konsul George Jorck & Hustru Emma Jorck's Fond

Danish Arts Foundation

FONDATION JAN MICHALSKI POUR L'ECRITURE ET LA LITTERATURE

KONSUL GEORGE JORCK OG HUSTRU EMMA JORCK'S FOND

A CIP catalogue record for this book is available from the British Library
ISBN 978-1-915267-11-5

Lolli Editions
New Wing, 44
Somerset House
Strand
London WC2R 1LA
United Kingdom
www.lollieditions.com